MY PREFECT COUSIN

MY PREFECT COUSIN

A short biography of
PAUL HAMILTON

by Kevin Eldon

FABER & FABER

First published in 2014
by Faber & Faber Ltd
Bloomsbury House
74–77 Great Russell Street
London WC1B 3DA

Typeset by Faber & Faber Ltd
Printed in the UK by CPI Group Ltd, Croydon, CR0 4YY

A CIP record for this book
is available from the British Library

ISBN 978–0–571–28311–8

2 4 6 8 10 9 7 5 3 1

CONTENTS

RECEIVING THE BRIEF

When my agent contacted me in early 2011 to inform me that the publishers Faber & Faber were interested in having me in for 'a little chat', I felt a rush of tingling excitement. This was indeed a very pleasant surprise. An avid reader since childhood, I was one of those many people who had always idly speculated to themselves that probably, when they had the time and 'a really good idea', they would at some point clear their desk, roll up their sleeves and Write A Book.

I had been enjoying something of a surge of interest from all kinds of quarters following a fairly successful run of my first-ever one-man show at the Edinburgh Festival the previous summer. And now, it seemed, an actual publisher – Faber & Faber, no less, brokers of such literary luminaries as T. S. Eliot, Kazuo Ishiguro, Seamus Heaney and Ted Hughes – had obviously caught wind of how good I was with words and languagey stuff and all that kind of hoo-ha and decided, 'This Eldon chap must be snapped up.'

Flattered as I was, after the initial thrill more sober thoughts began to occur. What did I have to offer this esteemed institution exactly? Nothing definitive, as far as I could see. A showbiz autobiography didn't seem a realistic option: I hadn't appeared regularly on any panel shows, I had no connection with reality TV, nor had I ever been a topless model. And anyway, at fifty years of age I was far too old for the celeb autobiography game. As we all know, if you're beyond thirty you're way over the hill as far as that particular branch of modern culture is concerned. On top of all that, surely I was ineligible anyway due to my ability to write fairly coherent sentences in English all by myself?

I turned my thoughts to the possibility of writing a biography about someone else. I have long been a fan of the popular Liverpool pop combo the Beatles. Could I perhaps write about them? Ah, but what, in an already oversubscribed market, could I bring to the table that was fresh and new? True, I had once talked to a taxi driver who, in September of 1963, had fallen into conversation with John Lennon in the canteen of Teddington Lock studios. He had told Lennon that his girlfriend was a Scouser. On hearing this, Lennon had turned to the other Beatles and remarked, 'Hear that, lads? He's nicked one of our birds!'

It's a fascinating story, gritty, witty and charming, but could I eke an entire book out of it? My gloomy conclusion was that I could not.

And that left The Novel. Had I a novel in me? Over the years I'd occasionally put half a mind to the task, but I'd never got much further than the vaguest of notions:

- There's this man. During the novel he changes in some way.
- A ghost story, but with some really weird bits in it.
- Something about alienation in a fragmented world.

Quite independently of any fully formed contexts, every now and then I'd come up with a couple of fairly promising opening lines:

- Benji's face belonged on a totem pole.
- There's something about an octopus that brings out the mother in me.
- 'Stand quite still,' breathed Inspector Barnes, 'or lie quite still – for ever.'

Sadly, though, these few scraps were the sum total of my pitiful attempts to become the next Dickens.

It really did not look good. And yet, I reasoned, faint heart never wrote good book. It was time to apply a bit of the old positive thinking: chin up, steady the Buffs, and all that! Wasn't this in fact a glorious challenge? Hadn't it been Faber & Faber who had approached me in the first place? And now that I was being sought after, courted even, who knew what creative portals this attention would unlock?

Thus I felt my resolve harden. Or at least become a little less jelly-like.

I had never met a literary publisher before, but I had a very set idea. What had I expected? A bluff, slightly eccentric bluestocking in her mid-sixties, that's what. And, on being shown into Fanny Stott's office, on the third floor of the Faber & Faber building in Bloomsbury, I did indeed find my hand being heartily wrung by a slightly eccentric, urbanely exuberant bluestocking in her mid-sixties.

Fanny was charming and very upbeat. She had 'heard great things'. I don't know what great things she had heard exactly, or even if they pertained to me, but I grinned, nodded and mumbled vaguely acquiescent half-phrases, hoping that my reactions were more or less appropriate. After what I suppose was a conventional period of genial chit-chat, she got down to business.

There was, apparently, currently something of a buzz about me. But not, she toothily informed me, quite enough of a buzz to set the hive a-trembling. However, she went on, I did constitute half a buzz which, if joined up with another half a buzz, could amount to an entire buzz that would set the bee-keepers a-scurrying. And everyone, simply *everyone* loves honey, don't they!

She paused here, regarding me with a lopsided grin and eyebrows raised to nearly above her head. This was awkward. I was clearly expected to offer some sort of retort, but in fact I had absolutely no idea what she was banging on about. Just nodding slightly and giggling feebly was, I felt sure, not going to move things on. I prayed desperately for some clarification. And then it came. Four syllables. One name.

'Paul Hamilton,' she said.

Paul Hamilton. Poet. Unpublished. Unpublished poet and, incidentally, my cousin. I couldn't really grasp the thrust of Fanny's plan. What was the interest here? I mean, Paul Hamilton? Who? That would be the reaction of most people to whom you might mention his name. So why was he suddenly a topic for discussion regarding the subject of a book? I knew for a fact that Paul had been trying for years, with an unflagging lack of success, to get his poetry published with any and every publisher he could point his mouse at, including Faber & Faber, and had been very vocal in his frustration at their refusal to appreciate his art. I certainly understood their reservations. Paul's poetry (like all poetry, of course) creates a very subjective reaction. And (like all poetry, of course) not always an entirely positive one.

Fanny, however, was all fired up.

'The moment I found out you and he are related to each other I thought, "Now *there's* an intriguing possibility." The thing is, Kevin, I really do feel that we at Faber & Faber are highly unlikely to ever publish Paul Hamilton's poetry. But, that said, we would very much like to publish Paul Hamilton.' She leaned back as if all was now clear.

I regarded her from across the desk, mouth half open, my eyebrows raised even higher than hers. If that were possible.

She leaned forward again.

'I've only talked to him on a couple of occasions. At poetry readings. Oh, and he sort of barged in here once, demanding to be seen. But I've been to see him perform quite a few times, and you've got to admit, he's extraordinary, isn't he? Just extraordinary!'

I gurgled a non-committal. I had been to see him on two occasions, and although there was no doubting the sheer intensity of the man and his verse, it was all just a little bit too earnest for my palate. Fanny rose and sauntered over to the window, seemingly oblivious to my incomprehension.

'There's something about that level of self-belief,' she said, peering distractedly at the London traffic below.

'Fascinating, don't you think? Oh, and of course he's hilarious! I shake like a blancmange every time he opens his mouth!'

I found this hard to take in. With Paul's intensity comes a very dry seriousness, albeit dampened by occasional sprinklings of a certain whimsy. Personally, I had never, to my knowledge, been rendered helpless with laughter.

Fanny returned to her battered swivel chair.

'Think of it, Kevin. A man with an unbreakable confidence in his artistic worth who has, year in, year out, met with a total lack of commercial success and recognition. It's a wonderful example of faith in oneself. Of limitless tenacity.' Here she paused, eyes twinkling. 'Or, some scallywags might say, utter self-delusion.'

'Oh, I don't think he'd be too keen to be associated with the notion of self-delusion,' I said.

'Exactly!' she snapped, slapping the desk resoundingly with the palm of her hand. 'Thing is, you've known him all your life. You have unique access, as it were. On a number of levels. So,' she trilled, lighting what I can only describe as a small cheroot, 'here's the deal: on the one hand, there's you with your small but dedicated fan base from all your comedy malarkey; and, on the other, there's the phenomenon of Mr Hamilton with his little ditties and fascinating idiosyncrasies. Now, separately, to be brutally honest, there's little there that we would be exactly champing at the bit to put out. But yoke 'em together and . . . bingo! Hmm? Hmm?'

So there you go. That's more or less how the whole thing kicked off.

Walking out of the building two hours later that February afternoon, all of my fears and misgivings had been soothed away. I had been totally won over by Fanny's earthy bonhomie and limitless enthusiasm (not to mention two large glasses of a very nice single malt). I was to be 'published'! I set to dreamily imagining myself on the type of culture-themed television programme that used to exist but has been replaced by ones about really stupid fat people and their dogs. In my fantasy everything was in black and white, and I was talking in finely minted aphorisms about my latest book. The frightfully attractive lady presenter was throwing her head back in sheer pleasure at my devilish wit, and the picture on the screen was shaking a little because the cameraman was also finding me just great. Then my thoughts turned inevitably to the subject matter. I slowed to a dead stop in the street as my musings suddenly snapped back to the reality. The subject matter. Exhilaration crumbled into a vague sense of anxiety. Vague sense of anxiety curdled into a feeling of mild depression. It dawned on me with an awful clarity that writing this book might not be an easy process.

STATEMENT BY THE AUTHOR

Writing this book has not been an easy process.

They reckon, don't they, that the story of every human life is in some way worthy of attention. The drama and the comedy. The highs and the lows. The triumphs and the defeats. But can a person's life ever really be recorded entirely accurately?

In the end what's presented here is a selection of Paul's reminiscences, alongside those of other people who have loomed large in his life. I've taken all these and, in good faith, stitched them together in an honest attempt to make as complete and objective an account as possible.

Over the course of about six months, I spent day after day sitting with Paul, recording hour after hour of conversation. He himself also submitted hundreds of pages of details about his life. I'm grateful for Paul's thoroughness in dredging up many, many experiences, from very early childhood right up until the present. He could certainly never be accused of holding back!

I'm sad to report that Paul is far from pleased with my decision to leave out some of his input. He also takes issue with some of the elements I have included, feeling 'betrayed' by the simple fact that his telling of certain events sometimes doesn't tally exactly with other people's versions. I've tried to point out to him that my job has been nothing more than to offer a fully rounded account of my subject based on all sources available to me.

For all the upset, I think it has been worth it. Because this book, in my opinion at least, really does give, as far as possible, an accurate picture of a man who's hard to define. His name is Paul Hamilton and, as he says, he is a poet.

STATEMENT BY PAUL HAMILTON

Hi. Let me begin by saying how grateful I am that you have bought this book. If you have borrowed it from a friend or a lending library, I am even more grateful. My work is about ideas, and you can't own ideas, no matter what Bill Gates may say.

On reading the final proofs I immediately sought legal advice. I did not do so lightly, because I have managed to maintain a level of integrity throughout my life by working outside the established systems (with the exception of the nine months I worked in banking, and even then that was very much on my terms). It transpires, apparently, that there is nothing legally actionable in what has been written about me. Incidentally, I was charged nearly £10,000 to be told that. The law may be an ass, but it's an ass carrying saddlebags of cash. Mine and yours.

I welcome this opportunity of a right of reply.

There is no doubt that certain events as portrayed in this book differ quite markedly from how I personally remember them. For example, my parents' recollections seem to be somewhat at odds with what actually occurred. What can I say? There is nothing I can say. They are both in their seventies now and, hey, if that's the way they remember things, then that is their current reality and I have to respect that.

Certainly, my partner Sophie's impressions of what

has occurred over the years do not always sync exactly with mine. Can I just say that, yes, I may well have done a little subconscious rewriting of the script of my life here and there, as do we all from time to time, but let us also take into consideration the fact that the love of my life once went on a two-week holiday leaving a whole chicken roasting in the oven, and on another occasion lost a brand-new Alfa Romeo after forgetting where she'd parked it. She never found it again. I could go on, but I think perhaps for the sake of domestic harmony I had better leave it at that!

These inconsistencies are, however, but minor quibbles, inevitable casualties of time's great blurring. My main bugbear is the dismaying lack of accuracy with regards to a number of the author Kevin Eldon's own accounts of episodes in my life. What can I put this inaccuracy down to? Poor research? Playful mischief? Or a cynical attempt to produce a 'spicier' read by a subtle traducing of a blood relative in the pursuit of literary kudos?

You know what? I'm not perfect. I'm not a saint. There. So frogmarch me to a wall in a courtyard and shoot me, and, no thank you, I won't be needing a blindfold, and, yes, I will have a cigarette, but beware because I'm going to be blowing the smoke right into your face. I'm sure not even Kevin Eldon himself would claim to be perfect. And he'd be right not to do so. With his voice-overs for products containing palm oil. And his non-membership of a union. And his frankly racist 'Scottish' accent. So I accept I'm not Jesus Christ, even though there are portrayals of me in some sections of this book where Kevin Eldon might as well have been hammering me to a couple of bits of two-by-four.

Only, this guy's not one for cheek-turning, OK?

You must, of course, make your own minds up as to what is the truth of Paul Hamilton and his life. All he asks is that you let his poetry and the undoctored personal contributions he has made to this book be his witnesses. For they are infinitely more dependable than any weasel words or sly implication.

Thank you.

1

ON BEING A POET

I thought it might be interesting and useful before we begin our journey through Paul Hamilton's life if I were to reproduce here a verbatim transcript of a small part of a recorded conversation I had with Paul about poetry and what it means to be a poet. I think it serves pretty well to demonstrate how hard it is to define what exactly poetry and poets themselves are.

Recorded in Islington, 14 July 2013

ELDON: What is poetry?

PAUL: (*long pause*) You could ask a shelf-filler, what is shelf-filling? And that shelf-filler will say, 'Well, it is the placing of Brillo pads, Oxo cubes, cardamom seeds, etc., on shelves.' But . . . that's hardly the whole story, is it? There's a missing element that words can never adequately express.

So whenever someone asks me a question like 'What is poetry?', I absolutely feel that rather than start going on about lines and rhymes, etc., it would actually be a more truthful answer for me to take a handful of onions and lob them at a bus whilst, I don't know, urinating down my trouser leg.

ELDON: Do you think –

PAUL: Or someone else's trouser leg.

Pause.

ELDON: Do you think a poet is born or made?

PAUL: Is a poet born or made . . .

Long pause.

ELDON: Yes. Is a poet . . .

PAUL: Born. Born first. They have to be. Otherwise they don't exist.

ELDON: Well, obviously, but . . .

PAUL: But, actually, perhaps they're the best poets of all.

ELDON: . . . Which?

PAUL: The ones that don't exist.

ELDON: What do you mean?

PAUL: Think about a poet that doesn't exist.

ELDON: Well, I can't.

PAUL: Can't? Or won't?

ELDON: Can't. I can't think of something that doesn't exist.

PAUL: Can't you? Right then, close your eyes.

ELDON: Why?

PAUL: You're very tense, aren't you?

ELDON: No, I . . . just . . . Why do you want me to close my eyes?

PAUL: Close them.

ELDON: Right.

PAUL: Now, think of a unicorn.

ELDON: A . . . right.

PAUL: Are you thinking of one?

ELDON: Yes.

PAUL: White with a . . . a nose horn?

ELDON: Yes.

PAUL: OK.

ELDON: Actually, the one I'm thinking of is a sort of very light yellow.

PAUL: A light . . . unicorns aren't a light yellow.

ELDON: Unicorns aren't any colour, are they? They don't exist.

PAUL: Kevin, unicorns are generally held – in folklore, in picture-book descriptions, in . . . all sorts of places – to be white.

ELDON: Well, this one –

PAUL: Forget about the colour. When I say poets that don't exist may be the best poets of all –

ELDON: Shall I stop thinking about the unicorn now?

PAUL: Yes. When I say that –

ELDON: It was just loads of different colours at one point. The nose was green, the mane was brown –

PAUL: What I was referring to is the fact that being a poet is about tapping into potential.

Pause.

ELDON: Right. (*pause*) What?

PAUL: When you write poetry, you are tapping into unreleased energy, and until it's released and manifests itself in poem form, it doesn't exist as such. Some of those poems will be mined. Some of those poems will remain in eternal non- . . . minedness. Right?

ELDON: Ummm . . .

PAUL: And so, just as there are brilliant poems that will exist, there might well be brilliant poets that will never exist. And they might be absolutely terrific. They might make Pam Ayres look like Keats.

Pause.

ELDON: Don't you mean Keats look like Pam Ayres?

PAUL: No. (*pause*) Yes. Wait a minute . . . Keats . . . Pam Ayres . . . Actually, that's weird. Because she does look like him a bit, doesn't she? When she was younger? Have you seen a portrait of Keats? If you saw their pictures together . . . Wow. That's weird.

ELDON: I've met her, you know.

PAUL: Who?

ELDON: Pam Ayres. She's really nice.

PAUL: Oh, I'm sure she is.

ELDON: Why did you say that like that?

PAUL: Like what?

ELDON: A bit sneery.

PAUL: I wasn't being sneery.

ELDON: Sounded like it.

PAUL: No. (*pause*) No.

Pause.

ELDON: Anyway, where were we? I'm confused now.

PAUL: The world's a confusing place. Look at some of the soups you see around.

ELDON: Soups?

PAUL: Here's my point. Poets have to be born, of course they do. But are they born as poets? Or are they made into poets?

ELDON: Yes, that's the question I asked you in the first –

PAUL: Shh, because this is important. Let's leave aside for a moment that some aren't born because they don't exist. Ultimately, it's not relevant to what we're talking about.

ELDON: I know.

PAUL: So leaving all that aside and considering the question 'Can poets be made?' – that is, can you train a poet to be a poet? Well, the answer is no.

ELDON: No.

PAUL: No. So how do I, Paul Hamilton, a poet, have a natural access to poetry in its potential form? It's a mystery. It's beyond reckoning. No one taught me how to be a poet. I didn't go to poetry school in Poetrytown, Poetryshire. And a mad professor didn't put a poetry silicon chip into my head and turn me into a robo-poet. A robo-et . . .

ELDON: A ro-et?

PAUL: No, that doesn't work. Oh – a po-bot, maybe.

ELDON: Po-bot's good.

PAUL: Anyway, being a poet is actually in my personal DNA.

ELDON: It sounds almost as if you think that poets are a breed apart.

PAUL: Oh yes. As are plumbers. And driving instructors and . . . curtain manufacturers . . . and . . .

ELDON: Soooo . . . poets and plumbers and driving instructors and curtain manufacturers together form a sort of subspecies of humanity?

PAUL: Ummm, no. No, you're not listening.

ELDON: I am listening, I'm just not understanding.

PAUL: Well, there you go. What did I first say when you roped me into this?

ELDON: 'How much?'

PAUL: No. I said, 'Trying to pin down a poet is like . . .'

ELDON: '. . . is like trying to pin down a butterfly'. Yes, I remember but –

PAUL: Well, there you go.

ELDON: But butterflies are pinned down, aren't they? Sometimes.

PAUL: Yes, but –

ELDON: By butterfly collectors.

PAUL: Yes, but –

ELDON: On boards.

PAUL: Yes, but –

ELDON: With other butterflies.

PAUL: Yes, but you've got to catch them first, Kevin. And I think you'll find that this particular butterfly is pretty slippery.

Pause.

ELDON: Are butterflies slippery?

PAUL: This one is.

2

IN THE BEGINNING

Paul Eric Hamilton was born in Gillingham, Kent, six months before me, on 17 April 1959, to my Uncle Eric and Auntie Joan. The Medway area at this time was a depressing place, its drab grey post-war architecture only slightly overshadowed by its drabber and greyer pre-war architecture. If Kent was the Garden of England, then the Medway towns were the outdoor privy.

Prior to researching this book I had had only very sporadic contact with Paul's parents, but on meeting them again I was reminded how warm and easy-going they are. I had forgotten that, to Eric, life seems to be one long, rather amusing joke. Unshockable and naturally broad-minded, he has a most appealing guilelessness. Joan was always a bit more prone to anxiety. She puts this down to being blown across her living room as a toddler by an errant German doodlebug and, as a result, 'I know it sounds daft, but I've always had a sneaky feeling that another one just might be along any minute.' She remembers her pregnancy very clearly.

JOAN HAMILTON: I was sick from day one. Every day I vomited. And in the night. I vomited everywhere: on buses, in shops, in the street, at the pictures, mealtimes, in the garden. Couldn't stop. Vomit, vomit, vomit. People started avoiding me after a while. I vomited all through the actual birth, too. The midwife said she'd never seen so much vomit. And after Paul was born I carried on vomiting. To make matters worse, Paul was a very sickly baby. He was always vomiting. We used to set each other off. It was awful. His father was doing national service at the time. He'd come home at weekends, but quite often he'd only stay for a few hours before going back to the barracks. He couldn't stand the vomiting. That's why we decided not to have any more children after Paul. The thought of going through all that vomiting again.

Joan Cooper and Eric Hamilton had met literally by accident. Eric had been on his bike, speeding down Shooter's Hill in nearby Chatham, when he knocked down young Joan, who was returning from work in a nearby macaroon factory.

ERIC HAMILTON: She went flying. So did I, come to that. The bike was a write-off, so it wasn't as if I could have done a runner!

Curiously, it was to prove a theme throughout their long, otherwise largely uneventful marriage. Eric went on to run Joan down another six times over the next fifty years – happily, never with any really serious repercussions: twice with a car, once on a borrowed skateboard and three times with a lawn mower.

JOAN: He never did it intentionally. He just never really looks where he's going.

Thrown together by fate, soon they were dating, and within a year Eric proposed, and Joan happily accepted.

After finishing his national service in early 1960, Eric went back to the job he had had since the age of fifteen in the HMSO section of the civil service, where he worked steadily and contentedly until his retirement in 2002. His hobby of recreating historical wars using model soldiers has been an enduring passion throughout his life.

Joan is a keen knitter and has remained a permanent part-time fixture in the same Gillingham charity shop for over forty years.

I asked Joan if Paul had shown any early interest in poetry or literature.

JOAN: I remember when he was three we gave him a book of nursery rhymes, but he was absolutely terrified of it. He'd scream and cry if we brought it anywhere near him.

PAUL: I think even as a kid I sensed the cruelty that's inherent in nursery rhymes. They're filled with very dark, subconscious imagery. 'Rock-a-Bye Baby', for example, with its falling cradle. That is clearly birth imagery, the baby falling from the safety of the verdant canopy to the unknown below. It's expulsion. From the womb, from the garden of Eden, from Babylon . . . fill in your own cultural gap. Or, say, 'Three Blind Mice' – the farmer's wife cutting off their tails with a carving knife, that's very clearly a blatant emasculation fear based on pre-feminist misogyny. I think I was just intuitively tuning into all these very negative themes.

JOAN: It was the picture of the lamb on the cover that upset him. You know the nursery rhyme 'Mary Had a Little Lamb'? Well, the little lamb was on the cover of the book, and it really upset him for some reason. We could never work out why. It was a very sweet picture. Of a little lamb. He never actually read any of the book. He couldn't get past the front cover. With its picture of the lamb. He actually weed himself once when his granny got the book out to read to him and he saw the picture of this little lamb. We did laugh. He weed himself as he ran out of the room. I can still see the wee splashing on the linoleum. He wouldn't come out of the coal bunker for ages. Funny, isn't it? Being so scared of a picture of a tiny little lamb.

On the surface of it, Paul seems to have had a fairly idyllic childhood: his parents were happily married; he was somewhat doted on by his mother; the family was comfortable financially. Nonetheless, I asked him if he had been happy as a child.

PAUL: Happy? Oh God, no. Where do I start? I remember right from the beginning I was always being closed down. That was how kids were treated then by their parents. There was no debate. No dialogue. It was just, 'Put the scissors down.' 'Get out of the road.' 'Leave that dog alone.' Then, when I was eight, nine maybe, we moved house. It was very traumatic. To suddenly have to tear up your roots like that. To leave everything you've ever known and to be, you know, propelled into 'other'. I was inconsolable. I felt utterly displaced.

I asked Paul if moving to the next street had really been so unsettling.

PAUL: Listen, to an eight-year-old a street away might as well be a world away. I begged my father not to go through with it, but he said I was being silly. I'm not exaggerating. That was his response. There was an incredible culture of complete disregard for kids' feelings in those days. You were a second-class citizen under an unyielding junta. No vote. No appeal. You got your orders and you followed them or you were punished. And very harshly, too. Withdrawal of television was one punishment. Once I was not allowed to watch *Crackerjack* for three weeks in a row because I'd taken money from my mother's purse. Now, in those days – and this is going back forty years – *Crackerjack* was social currency among your friends. If you hadn't seen Peter Glaze wiping a custard pie off his glasses that week or, say, an appearance by Chicory Tip doing their new single, you were out of the loop, plain and simple. That three-week ban was quite simply a barbaric over-reaction. Sadly, just one of many, many others. And, by the way, yes, I took money. From my mother. Guilty as charged. But the thing is, I actually gave nearly most of that money to a tramp who'd started living in a bus shelter down the road. I've always been very moved by other people's suffering. And that has turned out to be very inspirational when it comes to writing poetry. That's why I find the misfortune and unhappiness in people around me an absolute godsend. But let's get back to punishment. So there was the withholding of television rights. Bad enough. But the main form of punishment was that I was sent to my room. Any minor infraction of the rules would result in me being sent to my room. Refusing to go to my room was one such infraction. But I didn't see why I had to miss, for example, *Play for Today* just because it was on at nine o'clock. No videos then. No iPlayers. Any decent programme was on once, and then if you were lucky it might get repeated on BBC2 three years later at a quarter to midnight. It seems unbelievable now, looking back. But there were any number of different chastisements handed out: reduction of pocket money, tutting . . . Very subtle that one. A kind of psychological warfare. I'd unconsciously cause offence with what I thought would be a casual comment – say, 'It'd be nice to see some Alpen on the table in the morning for once instead of another plate piled up with pig meat' – and the next thing it's tut tut tut. 'Tut tut tut.' I grew to hate that sound. Even today, a single 'tut' is like a slap in the face to me. But look, we've talked about all this, my parents and I. Truth and reconciliation!

No one teaches you how to be a parent. As far as my parents are concerned, I've forgiven them. More than that, I've even thanked them. Because I think without meaning to they actually made me question authority. And I'm not talking about asking a policeman what the time is!

3

GROWTH SPURTS

As Paul passed into his teens a very real sense of fractious-
ness grew. His father remembers this time with affection-
ate exasperation.

ERIC HAMILTON: Well, he just went so moody. It's the hor-
mones, isn't it? You know what teenage boys are like. And
the jostling. Dear me! If he wasn't doing it in his bedroom,
he was doing it in the bathroom. Caught him in the airing
cupboard once. One day I told him if he didn't leave it
alone, it was going to fall off! He didn't like that. I suppose
I shouldn't have said it in front of his friends. I got the
cold shoulder for six months after that. And the crying!
Cry, cry, cry! I told him I was going to have to start calling
him Paula if he didn't stop boohooing every five minutes.
What with the tears and the spots and the jostling there
were about five years when all he really did was leak in one
way or another.

PAUL: I was very insular as a teenager. Spent a lot of time
on my own. I had loads to deal with. I definitely had a lot
of issues which would build up and build up. I would
worry obsessively at a little thing until it became much bigger, and eventually I'd just have to let it all out. I was often in quite a mess up there in my room. I think, looking
back, those years were actually the ones that essentially
defined me for the rest of my life.

Paul attended Gillingham Grammar School from the age of eleven to eighteen. He doesn't remember his time there with particular fondness.

PAUL: It wasn't until I'd been there a few years that I realised I was collaborating with a kind of apartheid. In those days you finished primary education by taking the eleven-plus. I was bright enough to pass, and accordingly I was shipped off to the local grammar school. If you failed, you were sent to technical college. Bad news. Technical colleges were where less intellectually able kids were primed to become factory fodder. Basically, you were reduced to a unit of labour to be used up and then spat out, and when you'd done your fifty years, it was, 'Thanks, old boy, here's your watch and a weekly pittance.' And that was that. Next stop, crematorium.

It wasn't till I'd been at the grammar school for a little while that I realised we were fodder of a different kind. We were expected to become the very people who kept the people who went to the tech colleges in their place. We were to be the industrialists, the politicians, the bankers. In short, the zookeepers.

It was about then that I started hanging out with a gang of mavericks and troublemakers at school. We all felt we were round pegs in square holes, and looking back we were always getting into some scrape or another. We were pretty full on. We all had silly nicknames. I was 'The Ham'. But, typical me, in the end it turned out I was the maverick's maverick. Even they couldn't handle . . . how can I put this . . . the level of my particular individuality. That was when I realised that enigmae can make people very uptight. They treated me pretty shoddily, but, you know, I'm sure after all these years they feel pretty bad about it. I bear no grudge. 'What doesn't kill you makes you a poet' is one of my maxims.

I was intrigued to hear about this period in Paul's life. After a little research using Facebook and other social media, I tracked down one of Paul's co-mavericks from Gillingham Grammar School. Anthony Holland QC (known as 'Dutch' in his school years) recalls Paul in some detail, and during an interview in his chambers in between cases he offered some truly interesting insights.

ANTHONY 'DUTCH' HOLLAND: There were four of us who had come from the same prep school and so were quite thick with each other. The Ham, as we called him, just started hanging around with us in the first year of Grammar while we were all involved in the school play: a production of *The Wind in the Willows*. We called him The Ham because he seemed to think that great acting was making himself blub like a girl. He was playing the engine driver. He only had a few lines, but every time he did them he could hardly get them out for weeping. Actually, thinking back, he did generally blub quite a bit. We found it all rather embarrassing.

I asked him about the kind of mischief their gang of rebels got up to.

ANTHONY 'DUTCH' HOLLAND: I don't know about 'rebels'. We weren't really rebels as such. I remember we complained to the teacher who ran the chess club because he'd put the subscriptions up. He said something about lost pieces not paying for themselves, and so we wrote a letter to the deputy head about it. That caused a bit of a stink. And I suppose I was always getting ticked off for having my top button undone. I'm trying to think. Apart from maybe Bonzer getting sent home for writing 'Pliny Stinks' in Latin above a urinal in the boys' loos, we bumped along without too much bother generally. So I'm not sure you could really describe us as 'rebels'. I mean, two of our little group were eventually made prefects, for goodness' sake. I think you'll find your average grammar-school prefect in those days was unlikely to be a rule-flouting anarchist!

I asked him who of their 'little group' had been made prefects. One was Richard 'Inky' Woollard and the other none other than Paul 'The Ham' Hamilton himself. But more about that later. First I asked 'Dutch' about what led to them falling out.

ANTHONY 'DUTCH' HOLLAND: It was quite extraordinary, actually. As I said, there had been the four of us who'd known each other since the year dot – me, Inky, Bonzer and Tadpole – and suddenly we had this odd little creature following us about everywhere we went. He really did talk the most awful rot. About himself mostly. But we tolerated him. Well, Tadpole did. But that's Tadpole for you; kindness has always been his byword. He's now something quite high up in the Red Cross, I believe. Anyway, the day came when this irritating buffoon just went too far. It was one lunchtime close to the summer holidays at the end of the fifth year. Beautiful day. We were all very hot, lazing about on the grass, and he was just going on and on and on. About how many girls he was going to do what to over the holidays and how he was going to be bigger than David Bowie and giving us his bloody awful impressions of Denis Healey. And in between all this he was having a pop at us. He was always doing that. Going on about how boring we were, apparently, because we wouldn't go along with his stupid ideas. I mean really stupid ideas, like all having matching umbrellas or clubbing together to buy the headmaster a Christmas present. He'd have no problem with telling me that I was fat and Tadpole was puny and Inky was stupid and Bonzer was ugly. Well, in fact, I played rugger and I was all muscle, Tadpole was the hundred-yard-dash schoolboy county champion, Inky is now a lecturer on neurosurgery, and Bonzer was having his pick of the girls from the convent school up the road. I shall never forget the moment when we all caught each other's eye as this twerp was prattling on. It was all completely unspoken between us. We'd had five years of it. And we'd had enough. We stood up, dragged him to the groundsman's shed, poured a tray of white-line marker over him and then carried him to the pavilion, threw him in the showers, turned on the cold taps and made him stay in there till the bell went. We were a bit shell-shocked at ourselves actually. This just wasn't the type of behaviour we'd ever indulged in, you see. It all felt a bit *Lord of the Flies*. But the technical term is 'justifiable provocation'. We weren't the first to lose our rag, by the way. Over the preceding years he'd been defenestrated by the debating society, he'd had his head pushed into a vat of custard by a dinner lady and he'd been punched on the nose by the RE teacher. He was not best pleased by our actions, of course. We thought he'd go straight to the head and turn us in. Seems he opted for the long game. The next term he had the ideal opportunity to get his revenge, when he got his prefect's badge.

PAUL: Well, it's the age-old story, isn't it? 'Keep your friends close to you, keep your enemies even closer.' And as the powers that be most definitely saw someone like me as an enemy, they tried to put me in their pocket. Oh, they gave me all the usual baloney. How I had great potential but was wasting it, and how responsibility would be good for me, blah blah blah. But I knew they thought they could buy me with a badge and some gold braiding around my blazer. They were wrong. Sure, I accepted their gaudy baubles, but that didn't mean they owned me. It would be *me* with a cigarette in my hand round the back of the canteen at break time. And I didn't even smoke. I admit I did hand out lines for running in the corridor, but that is purely a reasonable warning for something which can result in really, and I mean really, serious injury. The combined speed of two schoolboys running around a corner is twenty miles an hour. Think about that. You can't have that on your conscience. And if I gave detention to anyone I caught skiving in town, I did it out of compassion, not out of petty authoritarianism. You see, the only time I ever bunked off school I got thrown into the canal by a suedehead. I didn't want to the same thing to happen to any other poor sod. I may have overstepped the mark here and there, maybe not. I don't know – I am my own harshest critic. The point is, though, that if I did, it wasn't as a result of me abusing my power. It was as a result of my power abusing me.

I asked Anthony 'Dutch' Holland to expand on his claim that as a prefect Paul had made his former friends' lives hell.

ANTHONY 'DUTCH' HOLLAND: While he was a prefect he persecuted us. That's the only word for it. And not just us. Anyone he could really. As far as I'm concerned, if he'd been alive in Germany in the thirties, he'd've done very well in the Hitler Youth. If there was the slightest irregularity in our uniforms, he'd make us do a hundred press-ups. Once he found us having a cup of tea in a cafe when we were supposed to be doing a cross-country run in the freezing bloody snow, and he made us do the whole run twice while he followed us on his bike. During the time he was a prefect he made everyone's life hell. He only lasted three months before the head found out what he was doing and stripped him of the privilege. He left the school at the end of that term. Wise move really. He probably would have ended up quite badly hurt.

Paul seems wistful about that period of his life.

PAUL: I was riding a bull, and the bull was strong. I started off using the bull for good, you know, protecting cows, as it were, but then this bull started running wild and I had to get off before the bull jumped the fence and ran into the china shop. It was a scary ride. In the end I was thrown by the bull, but if it hadn't thrown me, I'd've dismounted anyway. Should I have got on the bull in the first place? Who knows. It's all such a long time ago. But once I was off the bull I knew it was time to leave the arena. And I can't say that I was sad to go.

4

PRETTY VACANT

Paul left Gillingham Grammar School in 1976 and enrolled at Price's Sixth Form College in Chatham, where he continued studying for his A levels in English, French and Business Studies.

As I've stated, while Paul and I were growing up our respective families rarely met. One meeting in the summer of 1977 does stick in my mind, though. A family wedding meant that Paul and his parents stayed at our house for the weekend. I was by then very into punk and new-wave music, and I eagerly played Paul tracks by the Sex Pistols and the Ramones. Paul had never been a particularly big music fan. Two years earlier, when we had visited his family home, his entire collection consisted of three Top of the Pops albums (shoddily re-recorded versions of top-ten hits played fairly amateurishly by session musicians), a Roger Whittaker single and a Showaddywaddy LP he'd found in a hedge. His reaction to the thrash of the punk beat was one of shock and then amazement and then enthusiasm.

PAUL: I'd never heard anything like it. It was so raw. So unlike anything else around at the time. Kevin also introduced me to all these punk fanzines – *Sniffin' Glue*, *Flickin' Vs*, *Gobbin' Spit* – and they were just so ... irreverent. That weekend I left Kevin's house a changed man.

Paul immediately embraced the punk identity.

JOAN HAMILTON: It broke my heart when he got into all that punk-rock stuff. He used to have lovely hair, he really did. With conditioner on it was as shiny as a girl's, but he went and got it all cut short and spiky. He looked like he'd been electrocuted. He made me take all his flares in. He wrote some awful things on several of his best T-shirts. His father put one on by accident once and went to the church fete. When the vicar's wife saw it, she spilled hot tea all over her chihuahua. Then he started behaving really awfully. He started spitting a lot. And not caring. He stopped caring about anything. I'd say, 'You've not done the washing-up,' and he'd say he didn't care about the washing-up. And I'd say, 'Well, you won't get any pocket money then,' and he'd say he didn't care. And he kept saying he was bored. I'd say, 'Well, take up a hobby then,' and he'd say he couldn't be bothered, and I said, 'Well, if you take up a hobby, you won't be bored,' and he'd say he didn't care. And that's how it went on. For months.

ERIC HAMILTON: I quite liked his punk-rocker stage. Upset his poor mum, mind you, but any time I needed a bit of cheering up I'd just have to look at him and whatever daft get-up he was wearing that day and I'd be chuckling away in no time. He looked such a sight. Of course, that'd make him quite cross, you know, and that'd make me laugh even more. I was quite sad when he packed it all in and went back to normal. Well, I say 'normal' . . .

PAUL: I was really into it for a bit, but after a while it got a bit wearing. There were a few other punks in the Medway area, but I was too bored to care about hooking up with them. And, believe it or not, not caring and being bored is really tiring. So I was actually spending quite a lot of time in bed. And the summer holidays were nearly over and I was due back at college for the last year of my A-level studies. Of course, at first I didn't care, but then I thought, 'Well, maybe you can not care too much.' I was starting to get bed sores. And I'd already lost my paper round: apparently my hair was frightening a few old ladies. When it comes down to it punk was dead in the water almost as soon as it had begun. It just didn't care enough. Which, of course, was what it was there to do. Not care. I suppose there was always that element of self-destruction built into the genre. Anyway, in the end I realigned myself with the new-wave movement. There was more caring there. Which, as it turns out, suited me, because when it comes down to it, as a person I do care and always have. I think the fact that I care is a big part of why I became a poet. If I were someone who didn't care I'd probably be working for Islington Council. In the department responsible for addressing the problem of dog fouling in the Islington area. That's a good job for someone who doesn't care. A very good job indeed.

Paul gained a C grade in all three of his A levels.

PAUL: I thought, 'Well, I might as well stay on the education treadmill.' I certainly wasn't ready for the nine-to-five grind, and besides – get this – in those days further education was free. Ask your parents about that, if you're a kid and you're reading this. And then ask them why they just stood aside and let them take it all away. When you've done that, stand well back, because that blush of shame will be very hot indeed.

A lot of guys I knew at school were already beginning to settle down. Finding jobs. Getting engaged. Saving up for their mortgages. There'd be no settling for me. I knew I'd outgrown Chatham. It was what it had always been: an uninspiring, dead-end dockyard town on the wane with absolutely nothing going for it.

Paul finally managed to gain a place studying English Literature at the Polytechnic in Portsmouth.

5

OFF COURSE

Portsmouth at this time was a depressing place, its drab, grey post-war architecture only slightly overshadowed by its drabber, greyer pre-war architecture. Here was a city which combined small-minded parochialism with the conservative conformity that came with its long naval history. Day and night great battleships and submarines would glide in and out of the harbour en route to or returning from another classified chapter in the long, shadowy chronicle of the Cold War.

During the week the locals all went about their largely unremarkable business. At weekends the pubs and clubs of Portsmouth and Southsea would be descended upon by staggering, roaring gangs of young, off-duty sailors. The ingredients of an ideal night were broadly agreed upon: at least ten pints of beer, some kind of attempted or actual physical contact with any kind of woman, an unfocused brawl with a complete stranger, the hottest curry possible and a sustained bout of vomiting in a shop doorway. Usually, but not always, in that order.

Paul was to stay for just two months.

PAUL: I'm surprised I stayed in Portsmouth for that long really. It didn't exactly have a lot going for it. There was the smell for a start. I'd never experienced anything like it – and I was brought up in the Medway towns. But it really did have its very own odour. I suppose I would describe it as a mixture of old cooking fat, Blue Stratos and rotten haddock. In the first week I went around asking local people what the awful stench was. And that brings me to the next reason for not staying. Talk about unfriendly. The response was invariably muted, if not threatening. And if I did get a reply, I couldn't understand a word. I'm a big fan of the sheer range of accents and dialects to be heard across these fair islands of ours. I went to Australia once. They all have the same voice, except that the women's are slightly higher. It's like audio mashed potato. I was glad to get back to our colourful tapestry of patoises. But the Portsmouth accent . . . it was what I imagined a stray dog would sound like if it could talk. Then there were the students at the poly. I'd come expecting to meet the vanguard of the revolution, and all I got was kids still living with their parents, listening to Supertramp, for God's sake.

Weirdly enough, it was here that I received my first direct exposure to a poet and poetry. It was an entirely negative experience. Having missed out on campus accommodation, I was billeted in a house belonging to a cheerful, blind, deaf, emphysemic divorcee. Another student was staying there – Valerie, a painfully thin, bug-eyed postgraduate in her early thirties. She was a self-proclaimed poet whose hectoring ultra-sensitivity brought me out in hives. She hated all men with a passion. And women. And children. She basically had it in for the entire human race. She was an animal-rights activist but was only in favour of animals that did not eat other animals. I heard her screaming uncontrollably in her room once, and when

I rushed in I found her cradling a dead woodlouse she'd found under her bed.

The landlady was obliged to serve up an evening meal. It was usually mince. In fact, it was always mince. Valerie would sit at the table, tears rolling down her face, holding a sign saying 'Murderers', whilst repeatedly intoning a poem of hers entitled 'Sister Cow'. I ate out a lot.

Her poetry consisted of pages and pages of utter drivel which she would read out loud at every possible opportunity. In classes, in the student canteen, at entertainment nights. In pubs. On street corners. 'Lion, Leave the Zebra Be', 'Maggot's Revenge' and 'No Wonder the Nazis Had an Eagle as Their Symbol' were a few of the more accessible examples.

It is not for me to judge another poet's work, but the worthless guff she dribbled out was appalling. If I'd not been particularly taken by poetry before my stay in Portsmouth, by the time I left it had, to my mind, become the medium of the maniac.

But it was the lecturers that really went beyond several shades of pale. Boy, did they like the sound of their own voices. And, boy, did they not like the sound of mine.

One of Paul's tutors at the time, Greg Birnham, still at Portsmouth Polytechnic and now head of the English Literature department, was at the time a new addition to the staff.

GREG BIRNHAM: Well, I was pretty idealistic back then, I suppose. I was always very much up for encouraging my students to chip in. I wanted lectures to be a fluid, two-way communication. But then I do remember this character coming onto the scene and just constantly piping up with the most irritating digressions. I mean, he'd say anything that came into his head. Totally irrelevant. After a while I started considering that he might be ill in some way. I actually went to administration to check that he'd been officially admitted and wasn't just wandering in from the street every week. The other students took things into their own hands in the end. I'd had more than enough of him by then and, to be frank, I was quite happy to turn a blind eye.

PAUL: I was effectively gagged. By other students as well as lecturers, that's what truly disgusted me. I asked at one lecture when they were shouting me down if they'd ever heard of solidarity? Someone shouted yes, it was the shipbuilders' union in Gdańsk and why didn't I piss off there? That's the kind of mentality I was dealing with. Finally, I was actually restrained from going into the lecture hall. I was physically threatened by two students. Violence is always ugly, but it is particularly unpleasant when it is offered by women.

GREG BIRNHAM: I reverted to the more conventional forms of lecturing after we'd got rid of him. I didn't want to risk ever going through that again.

PAUL: I took my grievances to the academic heads. You can imagine the reaction. Ranks were closed. Blame was deflected. Apparently the situation was entirely *my* fault. In the end I realised me and that place were never going to see eye to eye. I went to see the head tutor, and I told him

I was leaving and nothing he could say or do would make me stay. He was obviously stunned at the announcement. He couldn't even look me in the eye; he just pretended to carry on doing some paperwork. Eventually – and it took him about a minute – the best he could come up with was, 'Close the door behind you.'

Pathetic.

GREG BIRNHAM: We threw a 'Hamilton's Gone' party the week he went. Students and tutors all together in the canteen. An almighty knees-up. It went perhaps a bit far when an effigy of him was burnt, but it was without doubt one of the best parties I ever went to.

And so ended Paul's brief foray into further education.

6

BANKER

On 20 January 1980 Paul caught the 12.20 to Chatham via London Bridge from Portsmouth and Southsea station, back to his parents' house. Paul's return gave his mother quite a shock.

JOAN HAMILTON: Well, he just turned up out of the blue. Didn't phone or write or anything first. I didn't hear him let himself in, so when I came back into the living room after checking on a shepherd's pie in the kitchen I got the fright of my life. He was just standing there. I screamed when I saw him. He was very pale, with great big bags under his eyes. And he hadn't been eating very well, so he was very thin. So you see, just for a split second I thought he was dead and had come back as a ghost. I suppose it's funny looking back, but I very nearly had an accident.

ERIC HAMILTON: He wasn't a happy bunny when he realised I'd nabbed his bedroom. See, soon as he left for Poly I cleared it out and started using it for my battle re-enactments. Easier to get to than the attic. And warmer than the shed! I was most of the way towards setting up a complete replica of the Battle of Jena in the War of the Fourth Coalition between Napoleon's army and the Prussian forces. I'd got a particularly nice effect of the Rhine using silver paper overlaid with clear blue plastic. Anyway, sounds a bit selfish but I wasn't going to move all that lot out just because His Lordship decided he was missing his mum's cheese toasties.

PAUL: As soon as I returned I realised that I'd outgrown the place. I'd changed so much since I'd been away. I think Portsmouth does that to people. I realised I'd moved on. Well, I suppose I'd moved back, but I knew it wouldn't be long before I'd be moving out. Again.

It was in the summer of 1980 that Paul received a letter inviting him to an interview for the position of clerk at the Midland Bank.

PAUL: I couldn't believe it. It never for one minute occurred to me that I'd be considered bank material. I was always lousy with money. I spent it without thinking, lent it to people who'd never pay it back and I was forever running up terrific debts. You know what? If the events of the last few years are anything to go by, they should have made me CEO. But anyway, as I say, I was amazed to be called in for an interview. Mostly because I hadn't actually applied for a job.

ERIC HAMILTON: I applied for him. After three months of him sleeping in the attic, bringing bits of plaster down with all his moving about, I thought, 'Well, he's not going to be getting a job any time soon, so I might as well do it for him.' I was as surprised as he was that he got an interview. He wasn't too pleased, but I put my foot down. He wasn't paying any rent, and I know Joan was slipping him a fiver most weeks on top of his dole money. So we bought him a suit – nice brown pinstripe, I seem to remember

– and I drove him to the interview at the area office in Maidstone. Blow me if he didn't get it!

PAUL: I decided to grasp the nettle, as it were. The fact is, I was drifting a bit. I hadn't worked out in my mind what I wanted to do, who I wanted to be. If you'd said to me as a twenty-year-old, 'You're going to be a poet' . . . Well, I was pretty macho at that age. I'd've probably got you in a headlock and told you to take that back, especially after encountering Valerie in Portsmouth.

I had taken a brief interest in poetry at school thanks to the passion of an English teacher we had in the third year called Mr Jackson. When he was reading poetry out loud he would walk down the aisles of the classroom, marking the beat of the rhythm with a slap to the back of our heads. It seems pretty barbaric now, but the thing is, even today, if I slap myself on the back of the head repeatedly I can recite the whole of 'The Ancient Mariner' straight off – so, QED, method justified. I think, looking back, Mr Jackson had a profound, though entirely subliminal, influence on me. Of course, as a teenage boy it wasn't the done thing to like anything as 'cissy' as poetry. Even before Valerie I had convinced myself that poetry was nothing but larks and parks, and if it wasn't Wordsworth coughing up a lung on a daffodil, it was Cyril Fletcher speaking boss-eyed gibberish on That's Life. But going back to the bank, I needed to get some money together to get out of that house. To get out of Chatham. So I went in in my suit and tie, with my hair neatly combed, and I told The Bankman exactly what he wanted to hear. But it was in my head that I was giving the real answers to his idiot questions:

How do I see myself in ten years' time, sir? Well, sir, if I work hard enough I would hope to be a useful and effective member of the management team. *Yeah, right. Listen, ten years' time? I'll be freewheelin' in the sunshine, doing exactly what I want to do with no griffin on my back.*

What do I think is required of a Midland bank clerk, sir? I may be wrong, sir, but I imagine it is a methodical mind and total dedication. *Or, wait a minute: how about a stupid tie, a walnut for a brain and a few quotes from last night's* Terry and June?

What are my hobbies, sir? Well, sir, reading and music. *Oh and by the way: that's George Orwell and The Jam, Mister Clean.*

I got the job. But the only real satisfaction was that I'd fooled the sap interviewing me into believing I actually wanted it.

I was about to enter the belly of the beast.

Paul began working at the Rochester branch of the Midland Bank on 18 June 1980.

PAUL: I think they nearly got me, I really do. I think I nearly turned into one of them. Day in, day out. Same faces, same routine. There'd be the faintest charge of excitement about once every two or three months when the total sum of the cash in the tills didn't tally with the figures on the remittance slips. The whole bank would have to stay until the discrepancy was found. Nearly five hours once. It was almost always traced to a French seven which had been mistaken for a three. The manager called a ban on French sevens in the end. That split the staff right down the middle. I remember the union nearly became involved, but it all simmered down before it got too heated.

Apart from that and one of the cashiers being shot in the face by a masked man it was just routine, routine, routine. Time just dragged by. I felt I was literally turning into a robot. I remember I started dating one of the girls at the bank. Out of boredom more than anything else. But whenever we'd go out, all she'd talk about would be what had gone on at the bank. I'd try to change the subject, but she'd just bring it back to the bank. Gradually, though, without me noticing, she started wearing me down. I found myself contributing more and more to the banality of our 'conversations', with ever-increasing ease. We'd be sitting in a pub and discussing how much the man from the amusement arcade had paid in in two-pence pieces. We'd be in a nice restaurant and the sole topic of conversation would be whether the stories about new cheque-encoding machines were true or just wild rumour. The wake-up call, the final straw, came when she told me she'd nearly mistaken an Austrian schilling for a ten-pence piece. While we were having sex. I ended the relationship. It became awkward then. We'd bump into each other in the voucher cupboard, and the atmosphere would be intolerably tense. Or there we'd be, waiting together to see the chief accountant to have a large amount countersigned and . . . well, strained silences all round.

That was my life for most of the rest of 1980 – taking home my pay cheque, being the good little clerk. And all the while I was just dying inside.

There was one guy, Monty, who set me off on a different course that was to change my whole life. He'd been at the bank for thirty years. At the Christmas office party, a little the worse for wear, he said to me, 'You know, you should get out, get out while you can. You're young. You've got your whole life in front of you. Don't make the same mistake I did.' He said he'd have got out years ago if only he'd had the guts. I asked him where he would have gone to. He said he'd have gone to Tunbridge Wells or Canterbury, as they were much quieter branches and the customers were a nicer type.

I knew he was right. I was wasting my life where I was. I needed to take a leap. But in which direction? For some weeks I made half-plans, came to poorly thought-out resolutions, but finally I could see that I was just ducking the glaringly inevitable. There was only one place for a young man with a sense of adventure and a yearning for life in the fast lane: London.

If only I could get a transfer.

In fact, Paul's branch manager was extremely helpful in arranging the transfer, and it was only a matter of a month before he heard that there was a position available for him in the Brentford branch in West London. The bank found him accommodation, and by March he was ensconced in a widow's spare room in Isleworth.

7

UPTOWN BOY

London at this time was a depressing place. Its drab, grey post-war architecture only slightly overshadowed by its drabber, greyer pre-war architecture. For the first couple of months Paul felt very much alone in the big city.

PAUL: It was a pretty lonely time. It was not so bad at work – the idle, superficial, utterly meaningless office gossip gave at least the illusion of a kind of communication – but evenings in my digs were desolate. I couldn't talk to my landlady because we had little or nothing in common and, besides, she was too busy talking to herself. In the end, I followed her example and started talking to myself too, in my dingy little room. It was a short-term fix. After about a week or two I ran out of things to say to myself. The silence began to feel a bit uncomfortable. I was starting to say anything at all just to make the atmosphere less awkward. You know, 'That bed sheet could probably do with a bit of a wash' – things like that. In the end it got so desperate I took to humming in what I thought was a nonchalant manner.

Fortunately, Paul wasn't alone for long. Working at the Brentford branch of the Midland Bank was a character who was even more of a misfit than Paul himself.

Charlie Dodds was two years older than Paul and had been working at the bank since leaving school at the age of sixteen. Small and wiry, with a threadbare moustache and slicked-back hair, he brought to mind the archetypal black-market spiv. Even as a young boy he had had a Plan: to break free of his working-class roots. His father ran a fruit-and-veg stall down at the Hammersmith market, as had his father before him and his father before him, and although his father before him had been a male prostitute, that had merely been an aberration in an otherwise unbroken line going back generations. Charlie wanted to carry on being a market trader. But not in fruit and veg. Or in the cold. He had a good head for figures. He picked things up quicker than most. Why shouldn't he do well and, through cunning, hard slog, not to mention a certain amount of deviousness, rise to the top? But the Plan had been sidetracked. By life. As Plans so often are. Since he had joined the bank, life outside it had come to seem ever more interesting than life inside it. Inside there were overdraft forms, rubber thumb thimbles and assessment reports. Outside there was music, girls, beer and drugs. Charlie's priorities had changed, and now what had been planned as a ticket out of working-class stasis had turned into a means of paying for a life of Good Times. The bank was somewhere he had to go during the day so he could go where he wanted to at night. And anybody who was up for the ride, and who of course could also bring a little to the party, was welcome to join him.

PAUL: I thought maybe the guys in the London branch would be a little more hip, you know, a little more out there than the ones back home. That's how young and

naive I was. I know now, of course, that if you could transport a banker directly to the moon he'd still be a banker.
Only for a few seconds, admittedly, before the vacuum up
there made him inflate and then explode like a bag of pig
guts, but you know what I mean. The only difference I
could discern was that more of them had pasta for lunch
than at the Rochester branch. But there was one guy. Charlie. Charlie Dodds. As soon as I saw him I knew he was going to be OK. The manager, Mr Garvey, old-school type,
very uptight, very conservative, was at Charlie's desk asking him about something he was working on. Every time
Garvey looked at the paperwork under discussion, Charlie would mime headbutting him. It was brilliant. In fact,
Charlie was a little unsure of me at first, a little cool and
distant, but one day Garvey was at my desk and I started
doing the same. Unfortunately, I mistimed the headbutt
and actually caught him on the side of his head. As I apologised profusely I remember catching Charlie out of the
corner of my eye sobbing with laughter at his desk. That
was when he started being a bit more friendly.

Since the age of eighteen Charlie had been trying in vain
to start a band. With his ancient Vox amp and his very
battered second-hand Fender copy he had so far been
spectacularly and serially unsuccessful in finding the right
musicians to blend into a satisfactory whole.

PAUL: One lunchtime we were in the pub and he asked me
if I wanted to play bass in his new band. I said I couldn't
play bass, but he said that I could, anyone could play bass,

his mum could play bass. I said, 'Well, why don't you ask your mum then?' and he said he already had. I was kind of pushed into it really. He took me to a music shop, picked out a cheap bass guitar and amplifier, and I filled in an HP agreement form there and then. I remember being quite cross because neither of us had a car and I had to wheel the guitar and amp back to my digs. It was nearly two miles. On the way three dogs urinated on it and a quite intimidating Rasta tried to persuade me to exchange it for some old shoes.

The first thing I had to do was get to grips with the bass guitar. Charlie was wrong, though. I don't think just anyone can play bass. The instrument has its own very special role in popular music. Forget the obscene seismic death waves of the baseball-capped urbanite in his tinted-windowed dragster. Ideally, the bass part of a song shouldn't be discernible in any explicit sense, but its presence should be intuited. It's like oregano in a halibut bake, soap in the nether parts or contempt in a letter to the council concerning dog fouling. Hendrix and Clapton were superb six-string guitarists, that is indisputable. I'm not sure that automatically means they could have dealt with the four-string so well. The first thing I had to get over was the agony. There is no other word for it. You start pulling at those metal strings with your virgin fingers and within days they're blistered; within a week they're bloodied stumps. On top of that, I was having to report for duty at the bank each day, and banking at that time was incredibly finger-heavy: pen use, credit-slip tearing, money counting, telephone dialling, coin-roll opening, cheque stamping, typewriter tapping,

not to mention stapling, elastic banding, envelope opening and envelope sealing. Each little action sent sharp
shocks of pain to the brain and waves of nausea to the system. Sometimes I'd have to break off from, say, bagging up
fifty-pence pieces because I was afraid I was going to faint.
But I stuck with it, even though there was a time when I
began to look upon that instrument not as an instrument
of music, but as one of torture. Gradually, though, as my
resolve toughened so did my fingertip skin, and then, one
day, I noticed that I wasn't grimacing as I was playing. The
grimace had become a smile.

8

ELASTIC BANDS

PAUL: Charlie was very much in charge of proceedings. He was the singer and guitarist. He wrote the songs. What he said went. There was definitely an ego there. When I joined, he'd just sacked his entire band for saying they didn't like the new name he'd come up with, which was Champion Charlie and the Useless Wankers. I could see their point. This dismissal of group members was entirely usual. The line-ups changed with the weather. I myself was sacked and reinstated dozens of times. Even so, I was the closest thing he ever had to a permanent band member, beside himself.

If the line-ups were unstable, then so were the constant lurches in different musical and stylistic directions. Charlie was forever trying to nail down a new sound, a different look, an original feel.

Charlie and I began to work on a new set of songs he had written. He'd decided that it was time for a glam-rock revival. I was nonplussed. Don't forget, this was 1981. Glam rock was about as unfashionable as you could get then. But that was Charlie for you. He just didn't care. The new band was to be called Silverdust. We advertised in the music papers for two drummers and another guitarist. The response wasn't overwhelming. In fact, the only people to answer it were a sixteen-year-old guitarist who'd just started playing and a drummer who was about fifty, weighed about thirty stone and had played mostly trad jazz. But beggars can't be choosers. The sixteen-year-old, who I never heard say a single word in all the time he was in the band, was picked up by his father from rehearsals at nine o'clock sharp, and the drummer was usually horribly drunk and had appalling body odour. After rehearsing quite intensely for a couple of months we finally got a gig at the Turnham Green working men's club.

I still remember that cold Thursday night in October 1981. My first live performance. I was incredibly nervous. I still have the set list from that gig in that low-ceilinged, smoky club full of dockers, bus drivers and factory workers and their wives and girlfriends. We were to follow a 'blue' (racist, homophobic, sexist) comedian just before and after the bingo.

The set list reads:

'Electric Boogie Superman'
'Wet Dream Deirdre'
'Do the Silverdust'
'These Flares Are Made for Flappin''
'I Wanna Do It with You'
'Mister Mental'
'Johnny B. Goode'

What Charlie hadn't told us was that our two sets were expected to last an hour and a half each. In all, the seven songs we had lasted about twenty minutes, twenty-five if we kept the lead breaks going in Johnny B. Goode. Charlie told us that once we'd finished the set we should just start it again – no one would notice.

It wasn't an auspicious start to my stint as a rock 'n' roller. We weren't helped by the fact that Charlie had insisted we wear the stage costumes his mother had run up for us. They consisted of red velour flares, red velour open-necked shirts and massive winged shoulder pads. All of these had been daubed in Pritt Stick before receiving a dusting of red glitter. He'd also demanded that we put on blusher and lipstick. To say that the atmosphere in the club was macho is an understatement. They simply weren't prepared to give us any serious consideration. As soon as we took to the stage the hectoring began. We never had to repeat the set because by the third song there were two old Teddy boys on stage pouring beer on my head, the drummer was so drunk he'd gone into automatic drum-solo mode, the guitarist had run off and was hiding in the toilet, and Charlie was in a fist fight with the club's entertainments manager, who had been beckoning to us to get off the stage since the end of the first song. We were literally thrown out of the club onto the street, our equipment dumped on the pavement with us.

And my reaction to this debacle?

I was smitten. This was unlike any experience I had ever had, and I loved it.

The next day at the bank, as I was checking a new batch of ten-pound notes for counterfeits , it dawned on me that something profound had happened. I had become a convert. A convert to rock and roll. And that felt mighty fine.

Over the next four and a half years Paul was Charlie's faithful bass man in a long procession of mostly short-lived musical collaborations that played scores of one-off gigs, residencies, mini-tours, headline and support slots.

PAUL: It's impossible to remember a lot of what we did. I've been trying to think back to some of those crazy bands, going through a few of the old photos I've got. The record's far from complete, but here's a taster of some of the musical adventures we had.

SOCKET CITY

This was just me and Charlie. He wanted to try and go completely electric and minimal. We both had Bontempi keyboards. Songs weren't allowed to have more than one chord. For lyrics we read out instruction manuals for electrical items in unison, reading the foreign translations as well. I think he was trying to out-Kraftwerk Kraftwerk.

LAKE

This was Charlie's attempt at prog rock. Again, disastrously out of step with the music of the time. He made us all wear capes. We only had one song, 'Temptations of Dionysus', but it was nearly three hours long.

ANEURISM

This was our foray into thrash metal. We found an amazing drummer who called himself Demon. Six foot five, massive guy, huge kit. He actually had three bass drums. We came up with a pretty good set, musically very tight, even though lyrically I saw a side of Charlie that I wasn't entirely comfortable with. I still remember some of the songs: 'There's a Party Tonight and Satan's Been Invited', 'Zombie Sex', 'Worms in Your Eyes', 'Drowning in Shit', 'Kitten Fuck'. We were all lined up for quite a big gig at a comic convention in Birmingham, supporting a German metal band called Schmerzengeschäft (Painshop), when Demon decided to call it a day and go back to work in his auntie's wool shop. We knew we could never replace him. I guess we didn't really have the hair right. And I knew that with my propensity for non-specific urethritis, jeans that tight were always going to cause problems.

PIPER LOUSE

This was me, Charlie and a guy he met at the Walthamstow dog track who played the trombone. Charlie had seen a programme on the Open University one night about Dadaism in the twenties and was quite impressed. We didn't have any 'songs' as such, just a series of different objects that we hit with other objects. An alarm clock with a golf club. A tin of soup with a rake. An empty bird's nest with a dildo. We would also extemporise vocally. We would, say, cough throughout one song, or list cheeses, or, you know, sometimes just do whatever occurred to us. There's quite a funny story attached to the name actually. Charlie just stuck his hand randomly in the dictionary a couple of times and came up first with 'piper' and then 'louse'. He stuck them together and that was it, Piper Louse. We advertised in the local press for gigs and got a booking at the Brentford Conservative Club. We were quite surprised but went along anyway. Turned out they thought they were getting a group called Paper Lace, who had a big hit in the seventies with 'Billy Don't Be a Hero'. It was a bit embarrassing all round, but they were slightly more friendly than the Turnham Green lot. They asked us to cut the set short – well, to stop playing really – but they still paid half the fee. Which was nice of them. Considering they were Tories!

Each band was to add to my taste for performance. For self-expression. By about the tenth line-up – The Dulcimites, consisting, I seem to remember, of seven of us playing ska on descant recorders – I was hopelessly hooked.

I asked Paul if there was any glimmer of his future interest in poetry around this time.

PAUL: No. Incredible, isn't it? I think I was still scarred by the Valerie experience. But looking back now, I do believe that on some deep, subconscious level I was gathering strength. Waiting to spring. At that time I'd never written a line, but I think it's significant that I started taking an interest in song lyrics. I remember noticing that Charlie's always had exactly the same rhyming scheme. So in a song like, say, 'Crab Town', which we did in a band called Alcase, which had a very pronounced Bowie influence, the lyrics went:

Sideways in a sunken alley, eyes are out on stalks,
Shell-shocked hooker reels you in and in her claws are forks.

And here's a line from 'Mister System', by our Jam soundalike group The Generation:

Your wife and children worship you, they've turned out oh
*   so well,*
But every morning you get on the eight fifteen to hell.

And a lyrical extract from 'Black Tulip', by our goth-flavoured band Guillotine Thrill:

Black the tulip on my coffin, black as black can be.
Blacker yet, the blackest thing, is death's eternity.

You catch the drift. I diplomatically tried to point out the rhythmic similarity by getting him to play the chords of various songs on his guitar, while I sang the lyrics from other songs over it. They always fitted exactly. Some people are very sensitive to criticism. Charlie particularly so. After about twenty minutes he threw his Gibson SG at my head. I remember it made a noise very much like the opening chord of 'A Hard Day's Night'. Ouch!

Tentatively at first, I started writing my own lyrics. I found myself enjoying the process. Little did I know it but these lyrics (there was always an accompanying song in my head) were my poem 'demos', as it were. They were pretty naive, and I kept them mostly to myself but eventually I plucked up the courage and showed Charlie a few. His ego didn't allow him to be effusive exactly but to my great surprise he did deign to actually use one for a concept band called The Pure Numbers. On the proviso of course that I didn't 'get any ideas'. I was never allowed to forget that he was in charge. On all fronts. Nevertheless, I was so proud to have my lyric accepted, even though it was the first and last one he would ever use. I'd worked really hard on it.

Albeit with the help of a calculator. I suppose you could say that it wasn't a lyric in the conventional sense, in that it was just the numerical ratio of a circle's circumference to its diameter worked out to thirty-five decimal points, followed by the words 'plus', 'minus', 'divided' and 'multiplied'. This was for a song called 'Pi and Maths'. This numerical oddity aside, I think it was about then that, even if I was still pretty down on 'poetry' per se, I was at least starting to get interested in words and the effects of words; the way they can tell a story, create an atmosphere.

Words are tremendously important to me. That's why I'm always urging my audiences to make sure that when they're listening to my poetry, they pay particular attention to the words.

9

SUBSTANCES

Paul asked me to ask him whether drugs had ever played a part during his time as a musician.

PAUL: Hmmm. Tricky. Well, the eighties were certainly a time of great experimentation and innovation, if you think about it. Suddenly couscous was everywhere, Ben Elton was saying what the hell he liked about Thatcher, and you didn't have to be Brian Eno to own a synthesizer any more. I guess I just got caught up in the hurly-burly of those times. As I've said, I was pretty green, whereas Charlie was very street-savvy. I kind of looked up to him. I did do drugs in the eighties, but it wasn't something that came naturally to me. For instance, I was never totally relaxed on speed. We did a fair amount of 'whizz' when we had our psychobilly band, the Mentalmen. We only did one gig as them and only played one song. When we'd finished it, Charlie was so wired he spent nearly an hour introducing the next one, by which time we'd run well over our allotted time, so we had to leave the stage and make way for the next band.

I think the drug we most overused was cannabis, particularly when we were going under the name of Daisy Roots Sound System. I've always loved reggae music. Johnny Nash and the Police are hot favourites on my iPod. So I was quite excited when Charlie said he wanted to start a reggae group. He insisted that proper reggae music can only be played under the influence of ganja. Now I've smoked a few herbal numbers in my life and – don't tell Mr Plod – I'm still known to very occasionally accept a cheeky puff, thanks very much for offering. Charlie's approach, however, even in those reckless times, was a little too excessive for my liking. Reggae is incredibly difficult to play. I would liken it to doing a tricky crossword, putting a clean cover on a duvet and repeatedly sneezing. All at the same time. And as for playing dat riddim high? Sure, it comes easy to a Rasta, but to a white boy like me, brought up on PG Tips and Swiss roll? Forget it. Which is exactly what we did. Once we'd hit the bong we'd forget the chords, we'd forget the arrangements, and indeed where we were and what we were doing there. I don't know what kind of grass Charlie was getting, but it made us all incredibly insecure. Once I'd had a smoke I was always paranoid about the keyboard player, because he had a bit of a turn in his eye and so I didn't know if he was looking at me or not. As far as I was concerned, if he wasn't looking at me I was worried that I'd upset him in some way, and if he was looking at me, what the hell did he want? The drummer would get paranoid about the rehearsal room's rather shaky floorboards. A Tube line ran underneath, and he was terrified that if he hit his drums too hard he'd fall through the floor onto the track and into the path of an oncoming train. (In fact, he was right to be scared. That's exactly what did happen to the lead singer of a New Romantic band, Paradise Sideburns, six months after we split. Rotten way to go.) And as for Charlie, he was paranoid about everything anyway, whether he was stoned or not: us, spiders, the government, his socks, the Pope. This was not the mellow smile-a-thon it should have been.

Daisy Roots Sound System drummer Geoff May remembers the pot-soaked sessions with something of a shudder.

GEOFF MAY: The amount we blew! Jesus. We'd be laughing like a bunch of mentals. We'd be rolling around on the floor crying with laughter, but then gradually we'd all get, like, massively paranoid because we suddenly forgot what we were laughing at, and then we'd spend the rest of the rehearsal all curled up and no one could get it together to be the first one to move, and in the end we'd only shift 'cos the next band had come in to rehearse. Once it turned out that the next group had been smoking some gear that was even stronger than the stuff we had, and when they saw the state of us that set them off laughing, and then that, like, set us off again, and then they got paranoid, and then that made us paranoid again, and then the whole lot of us ended up curled on the floor. Must've been about ten of us. We were there for hours. Mad times.

PAUL: I suppose the drug that left the biggest impression on me was LSD. Charlie had come up with the idea that we should try our hand as a psychedelic band. We were called General Love and the Sugar Telescopes. Like with the pot, Charlie was convinced that the acid would help us get into the head space of the music we were seeking to tap into. I'm not sure that the theory holds much water. I hardly think that if I had an affair with my half-sister, started limping and learned to speak Armenian that my verse would ergo take on a Byronic quality, any more than George Osborne's address being 11 Downing Street has turned him into a person with any knowledge of how to manage an economy. Oh, and if you're reading this any time after 2015 and you don't remember who George Osborne was, then just Google 'bloody idiot'. He'll be the first entry.

General Love and the Sugar Telescopes was pretty ahead of its time. Well, I suppose it was actually behind its time because its music sounded like all those cult English psychedelic bands from around 1967/8, bands like Andy and the Pandys, the Nuclear Lawnmowers, Blueberry Orgasm. But it was ahead of its time in that there were hardly any bands at that time looking back to that earlier time, and there wouldn't be for some time.

I was very wary about getting into acid. I'd heard that it was incredibly strong and could in fact drive you completely mad. I'd always thought that it was purely the terrain of the long-haired hippy, the de rigueur psychedelic accessory, along with the flower down the barrel of a gun and the poster of Donovan. What surprised me, though, was the discovery that recreational use of the drug had been popular among many established household names as far back as the early fifties. Although unsubstantiated, it is rumoured that famed personalities as diverse as Norman Wisdom, Nikita Khrushchev, Margaret Rutherford, Richard Dimbleby and Fanny Craddock were all regularly necking trips and spattering their ids across the super-cosmos in the fifties and early sixties. That in itself is pretty mind-blowing. Norman Wisdom on acid is quite a thought. I have seen the comedian Lee Evans often being described by critics and reviewers as 'Norman Wisdom on acid'. I do not think this is accurate. I believe, after my experience with the drug, that Norman Wisdom on acid, far from being an amusing, sweating, physically energetic clown running up and down a stage, would more likely have been a small man sitting on his patio for thirteen hours, transfixed by a piece of gravel.

I only took it once, and that was more than enough. It was in Charlie's digs, a one-room dive in an old converted Victorian house with a shared toilet at the end of the hall. Having rather apprehensively swallowed a tiny piece of blotting paper bearing a tiny coloured transfer of Superman, we sat and waited for it all to 'kick off'. Charlie had taken the drug before and was affecting the all-knowing nonchalance of an old hand. After an hour I felt absolutely no effect, other than a slight headache, and was complaining to Charlie about the whole thing being a waste of time. Five minutes later I was in the toilet at the end of the hallway, and when I looked at the walls I saw that they were crawling with bugs and dripping with hideous mildew, while the floor seemed to have a soft, viscous feel to it and the toilet was filled with a festering mulch. Disappointed that the drug was still having no effect, I was about to suggest that we have a game of Scrabble when I had an overwhelmingly convincing impression that there was a tiny horse's head at the tip of each finger, each one breathing a small plume of flame. I said to Charlie, 'Charlie, there are horses' heads at the ends of my fingers,' but being in one of his more curt moods he pronounced my observation to be 'bullshit' and left to go to the pub.

I was very uneasy at being left on my own, and yet extremely unwilling to leave the comparative safety of the flat. The slam of Charlie's door seemed to act as a sort of starting pistol for a veritable marathon of seemingly age-long sensory mayhem. Under the influence of the drug I was struck by two seemingly incontrovertible facts: the first was that everyone in the world hated me except Princess Anne; and the second was that there was a telepathic wasp hiding in the kettle, reading my mind. Those impressions were quite enough to be contending with, but accompanying these was a swirling kaleidoscope of mental and physical bewilderment: I had an obsession for quite a while that if I didn't think of the phrase 'Bernard's wig will soothe a quandary' every few moments, the entire planet would be eaten by a giant space-baby; and perhaps the most intense experience of all was my absolute certainty that I was made entirely of Bovril. And on and on it went, a rolling flood of extraordinary sensation and perception. When Charlie returned from the pub, the sight of him was terrifying. Under the influence of the drug his face, to me, looked bright red and bloated, and his whole body seemed to be undulating forwards and backwards. I asked him how long he had been gone. He said about two hours. I was very confused by this revelation. This is one of the stranger aspects of LSD: under its influence time becomes very distorted. Charlie had been gone for two hours, and yet it felt to me more like he'd been gone for three to three and a half hours. I remember as I sat transfixed I slowly became aware of Charlie saying, in a voice barely intelligible to my confused state of mind, that he had been to the pub to talk to the man who had sold him the acid, to complain that it didn't work. The dealer in question had confirmed that he had indeed been sold a very large batch of 'duds', and that he had received similar complaints from other customers and was going to go out and find his supplier and 'give him a right going over'. Having heard this, Charlie's story went round and round in my mind. I could not compute it. It was just so incredible, so amazing that out of all those hundreds, if not thousands, of 'dud' tabs, the one I took just happened to have been the only one that was the real thing. Coincidence? Kismet? All I know is that after my indescribable, extraordinary, brain-bursting, life-changing journey into the unknown, I have never again been able to bear the sight, smell or taste of Bovril.

Would I recommend taking LSD? It's a matter of personal choice of course, but if you are considering taking it I urge you to think very long and hard before you do. Because you won't be able to think long or hard afterwards. You'll be too busy licking a lampshade.

Of course, many drugs are addictive. Very luckily for me, I have always been into a drug whose strength and addictiveness other drugs could never hope to compete with. That drug is life. I have to have life. Without it I'd simply be dead.

10

CHECKING OUT

It was in early 1983 that Paul's tenure as a remittance clerk at the Midland Bank finally came to an end.

PAUL: I'd never fitted in. I'd never belonged. Sure, I became quite a dab hand at credit-checking a bankrupt, or reprocessing a prematurely issued banker's draft, or directing a percentage of an international money transfer to a third party, but I carried out my duties like an automaton.

The beginning of the end was when Charlie and I were offered a two-week tour of Portugal. We had cobbled together a two-piece cabaret band in order to play a few gigs doing cover versions. We were called Walkin' Tall. It was a good way of quickly earning the money we needed to buy a decent PA system. I had asked my branch manager, Mr Garvey, if I could move my two weeks' leave, and he had turned me down flat, but he had then taken it upon himself to offer me some 'frank but friendly advice'. Apparently I had the makings of a 'first-rate banker'. Apparently my 'musical hobby' was in danger of detracting from the 'focus and energy' needed to make my way in the 'competitive, thrusting world of banking'. Apparently the unofficial days I was taking off every now and then were starting to become something of a 'conduct issue', and if, as he 'suspected', they were connected with my 'pop band', perhaps I needed to make a 'definitive choice'. In that instant I did indeed make a 'definitive choice'. He had forced my hand. The morning we were due to set off on the tour there was no Paul Hamilton at his position behind the counter. I had phoned in sick.

I'll say nothing of the tour, save that it involved an unfortunate incident with a bad prawn and a still more unfortunate incident involving a pair of bent Portuguese customs officials. The aforementioned gentlemen enthusiastically relieved us of most of our takings for the fortnight under the guise of 'airport tax'. There was nothing we could do. Their guns were even bigger than their moustaches.

Walkin' Tall came back to England Feelin' Low.

On my return to the bank I was immediately summoned to the manager's office. I was to be dismissed. I was momentarily stunned. I never thought that he would actually dare to do it. But the shock didn't last for long. There was no way I was going to be seen just meekly accepting my dismissal. Did I slink out of his office, my head bowed low? No, I did not. Oh no. I squared up to him and asked him if he would reconsider. He said he would not. Of course he wouldn't. I'd scribbled all over his rule book, and rule number one in the rule book is no scribbling over the rule book. But I was not going to go quietly. I went to the union and succeeded in getting them to fight on my behalf for a claim of victimisation and unfair dismissal.

Of course, the sole reason for this was to waste the bank's time. I'd have a little fun with them before I walked away, toy with them like a kitten with a frog. Even if the dismissal had been overturned, nothing would have persuaded me to return. There was little chance of that scenario, though.

By the time I got to the tribunal the well-greased mechanisms of the Establishment had swung into action. Secret phone calls had already been made. Memos sent. Masonic handshakes exchanged. Before they retired to discuss their verdict, they asked me if I had anything I wanted to say.

I still remember my crowning moment of defiance as clearly as if it were yesterday: I looked them in the eye and told them, 'No, thank you.'

That single gesture of contempt was infinitely more effective than any long-drawn-out speech I could have prepared.

I was not dismissed that day. I was released. The tears I shed that afternoon were tears of relief that I was finally getting out of the rat race. I may not have had a job. But I still had my dignity.

A new chapter was about to begin.

11

HARD TIMES

Though he applied for a number of office-based jobs, Paul's dismissal earned him rejection after rejection. He was forced to sign on.

PAUL: My landlady at the time had a policy of not having tenants who were claiming unemployment benefit. I was given my marching orders. I refused. I knew my rights. But she knew my weakness and exploited it. As well as sporadic bouts of non-specific urethritis, a violent reaction to cat fur has been the bane of my life. I only have to be in the same room as a cat and my face puffs up like a poisoned Russian oligarch's.

JOAN HAMILTON: I remember when he was about five he wandered into Mrs Trent's house next door. She always had at least five cats. Well, when he walked back in his skin was so puffed up and blotchy, and his clothes so dirty from rolling about on the lawn trying to itch himself, that I actually thought he was a little boy who'd wandered in from a gypsy camp down the road. So I gave him a plate of egg and chips and some lemon barley water, and I was halfway to dropping him back at the camp when he managed to croak through his swollen windpipe that it was him. Dear me! The gypsies all moved on next day. Imagine if he'd gone with them – he might still be living in a caravan!

PAUL: And so I would come home to my digs after a rehearsal, and my landlady's cat would 'somehow' have found its way into my room. It's not too much of an overstatement to say that she was waging a form of germ warfare.

Coincidentally, a room in the house where Charlie lived had become available. I took it. I had no choice. I ended up living in that same room for three years. There were six rooms in all, two of which were occupied by me and Charlie. Another was occupied by Aggie, a massive woman of indeterminate age who had a hoarding problem. Charlie had been in her flat once after she called downstairs asking him to come in and unblock the sink for her. Not only had he been unable to find the sink, he couldn't actually locate Aggie. The other three rooms were occupied by a Frenchman who was always in a bad mood, an old lady who said she'd once had her bottom pinched by Neville Chamberlain, and a dwarf called Archie. There wasn't a great deal of interaction.

Looking back now, it makes me wonder how I survived. The room was damp, unheated and virtually unfurnished. Back then weekly income support was just £18.

This was a period in my life which was a living hell. In retrospect I am glad I went through it. This is precisely the kind of privation that a poet or indeed any artist of integrity must go through in order to experience the darker places life can take you to. It was a necessary rite of passage as I made my slow transformation from just an everyday nobody to a poet. I am grateful for it, even though it nearly killed me.

Have you ever had to resort to eating pasta – economy pasta, mind you – for six days in a row, the mere thought of an accompanying ragu being nothing more than a cruel joke?

Have you ever pressed your face against a delicatessen window until the glass was wet with saliva and tears?

Have you ever felt so weak from lack of nutrition that the effort of cutting your toenails has turned you into a gasping wreck?

There's life on the dole for you. Every minute seeming like an hour, every hour seeming like a day. Dragging on and on as the rest of the world skips by your cracked window, full and fed, ignorant of your suffering. This was my life. The existence I eked out for the fortnight until my parents returned from the Canary Islands and I was able to call them and beg them to send a food parcel. That was succour I will never forget and can never fully repay. I can still see myself now after receiving that parcel, skeletal, crouching in that darkened room, ladling great spoonfuls of macaroni cheese into my mouth as I wept tears of gratitude.

Charlie continued at the bank. I didn't envy him the routine but I certainly envied him the regular income. I tried my best to make the dole cheque last, but it was calculated to give you enough to eat for a few days, and that was it. That's always been the case, now more than ever.

In 2013 Iain Duncan Smith presided over swingeing cuts to the benefits system. He was asked if he could survive on weekly income support. 'If I had to,' he retorted blithely. OK, and what happens when it gets to Wednesday and your pocket is empty and so is your larder, Mr

Double-Barrel? What are your options then? There's always road kill, I suppose. Or a root through bins. Or how about adopting the survival tactic of the wild rabbit and consuming your own droppings?

Would you eat a squashed badger, Mr Duncan Smith? If you 'had to'?

Would you relish tucking into half a cold Big Mac, Mr Duncan Smith? If you 'had to'?

Would you dine upon your own faeces, Mr Duncan Smith? If you 'had to'?

No, I didn't think so. And yet you expect other people to.

Hey, here's an idea. Maybe if you got your wish to bring back the death penalty you could kill two birds with one stone. Slaughter the criminals, cook them up and then feed them to the poor?

Just a suggestion. I mean, it'd be a nice option for people to be able to take.

If they had to.

Anyway, after only three weeks of signing on things quickly got desperate beyond measure. I had to work. My parents were not made of macaroni cheese. I knew that from now on whatever work I took would present further hardship and tribulation. For that work would unavoidably be an obscene squandering of my potential.

12

CAMDEN LOCKED

PAUL: I telephone-sold. I delivered pizza. I did anything and everything to keep a wage coming in while I rehearsed, gigged and recorded with Charlie.

There were some strange interludes for Paul during this time. For a short while he worked in a small vegan health-food shop in Camden owned by an ageing hippy who called himself Wiz. Wiz was going off to an ashram in Wales for a month and needed someone to mind the shop while he was away. Paul had been recommended by Archie the dwarf, who had got to know Wiz after being thrown through the window of his shop by a schizophrenic.

It was a long drawn-out job interview. Paul was instructed to come prepared with lots of information, such as the exact time of his birth, his star sign and an account of his previous night's dreams.

PAUL: All I could remember of my dream was that I had made a slightly impudent remark to Esther Rantzen as I passed her on a bike, which then, despite my furious pedalling, ground to a halt. I remember that Rantzen caught up with me and told me she forgave me, but as she did so she had tears in her eyes. She was nude but for a busby.

Wiz also read his tarot cards and consulted the *I Ching*.

He then asked Paul to wait in the shop until he had chanted his mantra and meditated on whether it was astrally 'cool' for Paul to take the position. Nearly an hour later he appeared from the back of the shop and told Paul that generally the signs were not good, but as there was no one else available and he was leaving for the ashram the next day, Paul would 'have to do'.

In the four weeks that Paul kept shop just two people came in: a woman who wanted to complain about the quality of the mung beans she had bought there, and a blind man who asked him if this was the massage parlour.

When Wiz returned from the ashram he announced that he had been taught a great lesson of life, and as payment for Paul's work he was going to pass it on to him. The lesson, apparently, was that money and possessions will only bring great unhappiness.

PAUL: When I told him that some money would actually bring me very great happiness, he replied that he had a more meaningful payment than money, and proceeded to hold out his skinny arms and fix me with a nauseating smile. I remember taking the situation in. Here I was, being ripped off by a six-stone man wearing a T-shirt which had on it a children's book illustration of a train with smoke coming from its funnel, above the words 'I'm chuffed'. And not only did this patchouli-drenched scarecrow want to rip me off, he wanted to do it by attempting to pay for four wasted weeks of my life with a fucking hug.

I am not a violent man, but that was one of the few times in my life when I lost control. I went utterly ballistic. I think in those few crazed minutes I experienced the state known to Vikings as 'berserker'. I rampaged around the shop, pulling down an entire rack of spices, kicking a packet of dried figs across the floor, and taking great handfuls of sunflower seeds and angrily flinging them hither and thither. Finally, to my shame, I threw a sizeable bag of lentils at Wiz, which all but knocked him to the floor, and then, horrified that it had come to this, I burst into tears and ran all the way home.

Shame and despair were my bedfellows for a week. A most unhappy threesome.

All the while, though, I was learning. I learned many vital things during that period of no-hope, head-down, dead-end jobs. Humility. Gratitude. How to unblock a kebab-shop toilet. But then came one job that was to play a particularly significant role in making me who I am today.

13

COMRADE COMMIE BOLLOCKS

Established in 1975, Boldgate Windows is a small private company that makes and fits French windows in the Mill Hill area. Mike Boldgate, now in his late seventies, is still the owner. It took a little while to get him to remember who Paul was, but once he placed him the memories seemed to come flooding back.

MIKE BOLDGATE: A poet now, is he? Course he is. Never could work out what he was doing here. Mind you, I'd never've taken him on in the first place if I'd known he had all them qualifications. A levels and that. He didn't tell me till he'd been here a long time. I mean, the labouring work here is so routine it'd send anyone with half a brain doolally. There was this lad I took on once, physics student, I think he was. He was doing his – what's it called? – his gap year. End of the first week we found him in a corner of the timber store, bollock naked and completely covered in wood glue, singing 'Once in Royal David's City'. And it wasn't even Christmas. Mind you, you couldn't take on complete clowns either. We had this lad once, and he was so stupid he pulled a paintbrush stuck in a tin of varnish so hard the handle came off and shot up one of his nostrils. So when The Comrade applied – that's what we called him, The Comrade – he said he had one O level. I thought that was about right. Not bright enough to get bored and not thick enough to keep walking into the French windows.

PAUL: On seeing the vacancy card at the Job Centre I had been told that I was overqualified. So I just called in at the company personally, asked for an interview and played the dim card. Spoke slowly, avoided eye contact, filled in the application form using my left hand. It paid off. They appreciated my making the effort to apply in person, and I got the job.

Paul felt instantly at odds with his fellow workers.

PAUL: If it was difficult pretending to be a lot more stupid than I really was, it was even harder dealing with the general crudity of speech and thought that I witnessed.

The first thing that shook me was the sheer foulness of their language. Let me state here that I'm no prude. The Gilbert and George coffee-table book has pride of place in my lounge. I once attended an orgy. And stayed until the end. But this was an extreme experience. To demonstrate, let me take the Hamlet soliloquy and rewrite it as it would have been expressed by one of those gentlemen one lunchtime, over their corned beef sandwiches, strong tea, Penguin chocolate biscuits and copies of *Whitehouse*:

> *To fucking be, or not to fucking be – that is the fucking*
>   *question:*
> *Whether 'tis fucking nobler in the fucking mind to suffer*
> *The fucking slings and bastard arrows of fucking outra-*
>   *geous fortune*

*Or to fucking take fucking arms against a fucking sea of
   shitty troubles*
*And by opposing the twats, end them. To fucking die, to
   fucking sleep –*
*No fucking more – and by a fucking sleep to say we fucking
   end*
*The fucking heartache, and the thousand bloody fucking
   bastard natural shocks*
*That fucking flesh is cocking well heir to? 'Tis a fucking
   consummation*
*Devoutly to be fucking wished. To fucking die, to fucking
   sleep –*
*To fucking sleep – perchance to fucking dream: ay, there's
   the fucking rub,*
*For fucking in that fucking sleep of shitty fucking death
   what fucking dreams may fucking come*
*When we have fucking shuffled off this bloody bastard
   shitty wanking fucking mortal fucking coil,*
Must give us pause . . . you cunt.

Of course, I'm sure for most readers the immediate reaction is one of shock. And I sincerely apologise for any
offence caused. I do not despoil the Bard lightly. I am only
attempting to conjure up the sheer level of profanity that
permeated every verbal exchange. But it is amazing not
only how quickly one acclimatises to any situation one
finds oneself in, but indeed also how one unconsciously adapts so as not to stand out from the crowd. By the
Friday afternoon of the second week, almost without noticing it, I had become as foul-mouthed as any of them.

Indeed, it was only when I asked, completely automatically, a perfectly respectable old man in the street, 'What's the
fucking time, fanny batter?' that I began checking myself
and curbing my worst excesses.

But fouler than their tongues were their hearts. Every
tea break and lunchtime they would sit at their benches
greedily 'reading' their copies of the *Sun* and paraphrasing
whatever hateful diatribes were on offer that day. After
only three days I had been christened Lord Snooty Bollocks purely because of my accent and the fact that I
had used the word 'determinism'. And this was despite my
attempts to affect a light Cockney twang.

I suppose it was always a long shot that I was going to fit
in. But still, it came as a bitter shock that I did not. I'd cul-
tivated a somewhat rose-tinted view of working-class people from my mother's side of the family. My second cousin
Derek, for instance. He was a plumber, cheery and cheering, always a joke on his lips, even when he was dying from
asbestos poisoning. Then there was Uncle Barney, a gentle,
genial, God-fearing man, a gardener for Lord Smethwick
in Hampshire who would have lived even longer than his
seventy-four years if he hadn't been trampled to death one
Bank Holiday Monday by the Bordon Hunt. These men,
and others like them in our family, were possessed of an
innate decency which conferred on them a nobility all of
its own. The jeering philistines I found myself shackled to
for the next two years, however, were a completely separate subsection. Emphasis on the 'sub'.

MIKE BOLDGATE: He never really stood a chance with
the lads, the way they were. Piss-takers, the lot of them.

I remember those first few days after he started I'd have to keep coming out of the office at lunchtimes to find out what they were laughing about. Cracking them up, he was. Talking all this rubbish, see, using all these posh words, making all these shit jokes. Well, it was a red rag to a bull. After that first week I asked the foreman how he was doing. He said, 'He's bloody useless, but keep him on, boss, please. I've never seen the boys so happy.'

PAUL: In those early weeks I knew that I daren't speak with my real voice and would have to severely limit my vocabulary, or the opprobrium would prove unbearable. I also realised that I could never bring myself to affect solidarity with their hateful views, so at first I just attempted pleasant, neutral conversation about what I thought were harmless subjects – the weather, say, or the difficulty of removing the varnish from beneath the fingernails. But it seemed that almost everything I said was met with suppressed giggles, which very quickly graduated to gales of incredulous laughter, accompanied by vigorous nudging and knee slapping.

Meanwhile, each and every day their revolting views and opinions would spew forth from their spittle-flecked mouths with tedious regularity, over and over again: gay men should be shot; union leaders should be hung; feminists should be hung, then shot; blacks were drug addicts; Asians were cruel to dogs, yada yada yada. Their ignorance and hatred appalled me and eventually galvanised me, step by step, into taking an oppositional stance. My first show of defiance was to openly read a copy of the *Guardian* newspaper during break times. That simple act of daring immediately elicited a barrage of vitriol about 'that commie rag' and that 'poof's comic', and indeed I quickly learned to hide it between breaks because otherwise I would find it defaced with crudely drawn ejaculating phalli or cut into neat squares and placed on top of the toilet cistern.

It wasn't long before I was taking vocal exception to their hateful opinions, tentatively at first, but slowly gaining in commitment and intensity.

MIKE BOLDGATE: Lord Snooty Bollocks. That was what they called him at first. Then, once he started sounding off with all this Militant Tendency palaver, that's when they started calling him Comrade Commie Bollocks, or The Comrade. I almost felt sorry for him sometimes, the stick they gave him. Trouble is, he was such a wanker, you couldn't help thinking he deserved it. Didn't know when to keep his gob shut, that was The Comrade's problem.

PAUL: I tried my best to reason, to counter their base surmisings. But how do you debate with a slavering mob? How do you advance an argument when the reply is either mastic sealant squirted into your tea or a slice of jam sponge thrown at the back of your head? What can you do when any word with more than two syllables provokes paroxysms of helpless laughter, with said word repeated several times by everybody in an effeminate voice?

It was a daily endurance test. Quite apart from their witless drivel, the job itself was, as promised, utterly without creativity or interest. I swept the floor. I emptied the dust extractor. I sandpapered wood. I cleaned the toilet. I made the tea. Repeat. Ad nauseam. And do indeed add nauseam. I found the smell of varnish to be truly sickening. The only slight respite was when I would be dispatched each morning before the break to the nearby garage shop to buy flaccid, grey-meated sausage rolls, starchy, pre-wrapped pastries, packet after packet of cheap, lung-dissolving tobacco, bargain-basement pornography and instant-noodle meals – anything, it seemed, as long as it contained no nutrition, beauty or worth. And at the end of the week a pitiful £40 or so would be handed to me in a brown paper envelope and I would exhaustedly cycle home. I was trapped. The recession was in full swing. There was literally nowhere else to go. I performed my duties tolerably well, although I was often chided and complained about, but I had one saving grace: they seemed to find me amusing. It infuriated me at the time, but now I see that their gibes, their hooting and heckling were a deliberate tactic to avoid confronting their own ignorance. They would never want to do that. No, far better to cackle with vicious gusto, honk with dead-eyed hilarity, guffaw in brutish glee until the voice of reason and compassion was subsumed in a cacophony of shrill contempt.

And yet and yet and yet. Until the first morning I nervously walked through the forbidding metal folding doors of Boldgate Windows I had been politically lethargic. Sure, I hated Thatcher, but only the retired colonels and the Normals in their ticky-tacky houses actually liked her. Hating Thatcher was most people's default setting. It's only with the passing of time and a convenient rewriting of her legacy that she has acquired a more positive appeal.

In that sense she is like trepanning.

Where do I start with that particular *bête bleu*?

The Falklands War. Are the Falkland Islands really British? Yes? OK, have you ever tried to get there by bus? Would we have thought it right if the Argentinians had just blundered onto the Isle of Man and called it La Isla del Hombre?

And then just look what she did to the mining communities around the country. I had always been fascinated by the idea of being a miner. The thrill and adventure of it all. The sheer romance of a noble tradition of working-class strife. Bare-chested men sweating in the dark, all pulling together. Well, Thatcher crushed that dream for me before it ever had the chance of being further considered as a possible likelihood. Thanks, Maggie.

Who was it who called the IRA terrorists?

Who was it who incorrectly used the plural personal pronoun when announcing the birth of her grandchild?

Who was it, for God's sake, with a well-known aversion for men with beards, who then hypocritically goes and chooses 'Two Little Boys' as her all-time favourite on *Desert Island Discs*, sung by – yes, that's right – the be-whiskered Rolf Harris.

The list goes on.

It was strange, wasn't it, the totally mixed reaction to her death. I can't say I wasn't undismayed to hear about her demise. On the day of her funeral I certainly wasn't going to mourn her. At the same time, I didn't go to any of the parties exalting in her death. Mostly because there were none in Islington (none that I was aware of anyway).

Perhaps this was just as well, because after some reflection I decided that the best way to demonstrate my contempt would be to remain completely impassive. In the end I spent the day engaged in emotionally neutral acts: I went for a haircut, I listened to some Neil Diamond, and I completed a new passport-application form. I wonder what the young Paul Hamilton would have thought of that measured response.

Still, the point I am making is that by the time I left Boldgate Windows after nearly two years of suffering its myriad torments, I had become Political. The Right was wrong. The Left was all that remained. It was as simple as that. And it still is, with the simple difference that there is no longer any Left left. The Left's Right now (except it's wrong).

Looking back and remembering the indignities I suffered at the hands of my co-workers, I guess I could be bitter. Being tied in a sack and then bundled onto the back of a timber lorry bound for Cardiff. Or locked in the tool store for the night. The dead mouse in my thermos. The live worms in my lunch box. The felt-tip-penning of the word 'knob' on my forehead whilst dozing at lunchtime. On twenty separate occasions. And a thousand and one other minor and not so minor persecutions. But I have come to realise that I should be grateful to them. And feel sorrow for them. After all, they were conditioned to watch *The Price Is Right* rather than the latest Dennis Potter television play. They were programmed to go to a pub and drink until they fell down rather than taking in a Cézanne exhibition. They were brainwashed into brawling on the terraces of some football team or other rather than seeking stillness and completeness in more meditative pursuits. I left hating them. Since then I have grown to love them, for all their crassness and crudity, and I have even shed a tear or two for all that potential kept hammered down from cradle to grave.

And so if you want to know why I recycle, if you want to know why I sign online petitions, if you want to know why I write to the prime minister once a month detailing my grievances, then put it all down to a young man standing in a circle of taunting oafs with a bucket on his head and his trousers round his ankles as they chant in a moronic monotone, 'Comrade Commie Bollocks! Comrade Commie Bollocks! Comrade Commie Bollocks!'

Thanks, guys.

14

BETRAYAL

PAUL: I have been seriously betrayed three times in my life. I was betrayed when I caught Nicholas Humphries, whom I had thought a friend, kissing Jenny Corbett, whom I had long adored from afar, on the lips at the back of assembly in May 1969, during the third verse of 'He Who Would Valiant Be'. I was betrayed when a so-called literary agent told me she had succeeded in publishing one of my poems, a paean to love, only to produce from her handbag a greetings card in which was printed just one of the twenty verses I'd composed, and on the front of which was a picture of a duckling sitting in a glittery red heart, under the words 'Happy Valentine's Day, Granny'.

Neither of these equals the seismic shock of The Great Betrayal.

Charlie had announced early in 1986 that he was leaving the bank. I was relieved. He'd been vaguely promising to get off the treadmill since I'd left so that we could both concentrate on finally solidifying our musical vision. I'd been on his case. I'd taken the leap, so why couldn't he? But summer turned to autumn and he still hadn't left. He was waiting for the right time, he said.

In late 1986 he dropped the bombshell. Yes, he was leaving the bank. But not in order to finally dedicate his life to artistic creativity. Not to get out of the prison of the nine to five and finally run free. He was leaving the bank to go and work on the London Stock Exchange.

That's right. He had landed a job as a trader for a brokerage firm.

I didn't know what that meant. I still don't. The financial institutions in the City of London had been deregulated. I had no idea what that meant either. And never will. Let's just assume that if it was to do with 'The Market', there wasn't going to be anything in it for the ordinary Joe. Unless, of course, you wanted to risk playing that game. And that was exactly what Charlie did want to do. In one fell swoop he traded Charlie the Musician in for Charlie the Money Man. Bad deal.

I still remember with crystal clarity sitting in numbed shock as he told me over a curry on the Fulham Road. There was more to come, though. Barely had the news sunk in when he further announced that he was leaving the band. What? Were my ears deceiving me? This was too much to bear. We'd never exactly been bosom buddies, Charlie and I. Our dispositions were at odds, he with his volatile temperament, and me with my more deductive, cerebral approach. I found his lack of basic good manners a constant source of dismay. And I think my inability to drink more than four pints of beer without being sick irked him. But still, we had been through a lot together. There was a very strong bond. Or so I'd thought. After he'd told me his awful news I remember I just got up and stumbled out of the restaurant in a shocked daze. He followed me out, urging me not to just walk away like that. I told him there was nothing more to discuss. He said there was – my share of the bill for the curry. I gave him £5 and walked off, telling him I was due £1.30 change and that I wanted it by next Monday.

Monday came and went. The £1.30 did not materialise.

We exchanged only a few words in the weeks after that. Mostly about the £1.30. By Christmas 1986 Charlie had moved out, and his room had been taken by an abattoir worker who was clearly emotionally unwell.

I saw Charlie only one more time after that. He called me early one evening six months later and begged me to come for a drink with him down at Canary Wharf. He sounded upbeat.

'Come on down, mate,' he said. 'Bygones be bygones an' all that!' Never one to bear a grudge, I agreed. What greeted me was a caricature, a two-dimensional cliché. With his Armani suit and his red braces, his £100 shoes and his expensively coiffed hair he looked every inch the shrill yuppie of tabloid notoriety. Charlie greeted me like a long-lost brother, introducing me to a group of other similarly dressed young men with names like Ashley and Gideon and Dave. Gone was his trademark pint of lager and lime. It was garishly coloured cocktails now. No more Embassy Regal for Charlie; they had been usurped by Dunhill International. And the talk, the chatter, the endless barrage of jabbering and prattling . . . I could not get a word in edgeways.

Ten minutes after my arrival one of them leaned in close. 'Fancy a toot?' he hissed out of the side of his mouth. I didn't understand. He went on, 'A bang . . . a bump . . . a line.' Thinking that he was propositioning me, I thanked him, told him I wasn't gay but was nevertheless flattered. He laughed a lot at that. Then he whispered to the others, and they all laughed a lot too. It was explained to me that I was being offered cocaine. I was shocked. In the eighties Bolivian marching powder was very much the preserve of the super-rich. It simply wasn't available to the common man. Nowadays, of course, one can pass any football stadium on a Saturday afternoon and witness mono-browed Neanderthals sniffing lines of it off the top of parking meters, but this was another age. And so, feeling under pressure from the group – and, I admit, rather curious – I acquiesced and took the small wrap of folded paper that had been slipped to me into a cubicle in the toilets. I had never taken cocaine – and, indeed, have never done so since – and so was totally ignorant of what it was exactly that I was supposed to do. I knew it was snorted, so I opened up the paper, inside of which was a smallish rectangle of white powder. I hoped for the best, closed one nostril and snorted the powder into the other in three large sniffs.

Well, of course, it turned out that I had ingested nearly a gram of a highly powerful class A drug. No one had told me I was supposed to chop off a small amount and nasally ingest that, so by the time I returned to my drinking chums I was already in a state of manic exhilaration. I thanked the one who had given me the drug about twenty times, until I realised he wanted something from me. The paper wrap. I told him I had dropped it in the toilet. He was incredulous, and then, after realising that I had in my ignorance sniffed the entire amount given to me, laughed even harder than he had before. After informing the others what had transpired, they too reacted with uproar, becoming so convulsed by hysterics that I feared they might actually lose consciousness. I was surprised at how funny I thought the situation was too.

What followed is a loose series of disjointed memories, linked only by the presence of Charlie and his friends laughing uproariously and the sensation that a live frog had been inserted immediately behind my left nipple and was trying to jump up and down on my heart until it burst. I remember a quick succession of drinks. A lot of talking. A large crowd who seemed to be hugely enjoying watching me dance. Some large men removing me from behind the bar, where I was, I think, unsuccessfully trying to mix cocktails with the same aplomb as the bar staff. A young woman standing over me and looking down with a very cross expression, wagging a finger in my face. And finally I remember standing outside the bar in the dark with Charlie and his friends as they said they had to be going.

'But before we head off,' Charlie said, pressing something into my hand, 'here's that £1.30 I owe you.' This provided them with the longest, loudest laugh of the evening. It must have lasted about ten minutes. They were bent double. They were weeping. One of them actually wet himself, and that extended the merriment for another quarter of an hour. I couldn't join in. I was becoming worried about the unpleasant tingling in my arms. Finally, off they reeled, their laughter gradually fading as they piled into a passing cab and disappeared from view.

I looked at the money in my hand. It was somehow comforting that my old comrade at least still had some integrity left.

And that was the last I ever saw of Charlie. In the mid-nineties I heard through an old mutual acquaintance that he had gone on to attain quite a high position in an investment bank. A dubious achievement, but an achievement nonetheless, I suppose.

If you're reading this, Charlie: even though you were often incredibly selfish and foul-tempered, and went on to make some disastrous decisions in your life which probably had far-reaching, negative repercussions for a lot of innocent people, you weren't all bad. In fact, I'm glad I knew you. Because, let's face it, didn't we rock? Didn't we roll? Thanks for all the good times, you old dog.

I was fascinated by Paul's tales of Charlie and quickly realised that as far as this book is concerned, any input from him would be pure gold. Sadly, despite spending a lot of time and effort trying to establish contact, I was never actually able to track him down. This much I did find out, though: he had indeed been a senior executive officer in an investment bank, one that dealt mostly with companies involved in armaments, pesticides and logging in the Third World. In 2003 he was arrested by the Serious Fraud Squad and convicted of embezzling over £30 million from his bank. He was sentenced to four years in jail, where he converted to Islam and renounced his old life. He is now happily married with three children and is living in Tehran, where he works in a market. On a fruit and veg stall.

15

LIMBO NUMBER 1

After Charlie moved out, Paul knew that his days at the place where he was living were numbered.

PAUL: The abattoir worker with mental-health issues who took over Charlie's old room made staying at that particular place a pretty unsettling experience. Once I opened my door to find him standing there smiling, with a pig's head under his arm. When I asked him if I could help, he replied that he wanted me to meet his friend, 'Pighead'. Another time he'd been found naked on the landing, asleep and wrapped in entrails.

It was time to move.

And move I did – aimlessly, listlessly, from one crummy, anonymous lodgings to another for the next three years. I was truly directionless. A ship without a rudder. An explorer without a compass. Simon Cowell without a dark, bottomless, satanic cynicism. Thinking back now, I shudder to think of the sociopathic housemates, the endless arguments about paying shares of bills or doing the washing-up or cleaning the toilet, the draughty rooms, awful decor, cockroaches, smell of cat urine, loud music at three in the morning, theft of food and personal belongings, violent neighbours, cracked sinks and flea-ridden carpets. That was a particularly bad place. But there were others too, lots of them, all similarly unpleasant.

All the while I was becoming more and more unhappy. There was one dark night near the end of this time when for the first time in my life I thought about suicide and, as I did so, I found myself realising that I could never, ever bring myself to actually do it. I was left with a chilling conclusion: there was no way out. That was when I became really depressed. They say you know you're depressed when you have no interest in anything. I'd lost interest in food, in reading, in sex, in music, in television, in radio, in world cinema, in personal hygiene – in fact, you name it, I'd lost interest in it. Apart from, strangely and inexplicably, seventeenth-century jam-making processes. I don't know why, but I suddenly became very interested in that. I was morosely reading the ingredients on a half-empty jar of jam that was in the kitchen by some tea bags one morning, when I found myself idly wondering if jam-making had always followed the same pattern. As I passed the library the next day I felt an overwhelming urge to go in and see if I could find any books on the history of jam-making.   There was one. I read it avidly in one afternoon and then put in a request to the librarian for as many as possible. There were five in existence, and I was able to get hold of a copy of four of them. *Jams and Jellies Through the Ages* by Daphne Stewart never materialised. I marvelled at the facts I learned: that marmalade was first used to keep seasickness at bay; that pectin was extracted from apple parings in order to thicken the jam; or that an equal amount of sugar had to be added to the fruit pulp before boiling. Perhaps my interest in antique jam-making methods was some kind of built-in defence tactic to prevent a complete shut-down. All I know is, jam apart, I was dead inside.

I guess these were my lost years. Or rather, the first lot of my lost years. I was to have another two bouts of lost years (although, admittedly, the second bout was closer to a week, so, technically, that's a lost week). That's missing the point, though. Screw the figures. When you're lost, you're lost; and when you're lost, it doesn't matter what the date is because every day is Lostday the losteenth of Lostember.

Many an artist experiences his or her lost years. For example, throughout the centuries innumerable scholars have debated the mystery of Shakespeare's whereabouts between the years 1585 and 1592. Did he become a teacher at a small country school? Did he sign up as a conscript in the lowlands? Was he employed as a novelty candle sculptor in Lincoln? The list of possibilities is a long one, but we have to conclude that whether he stage-managed a travelling troupe of dogs that could howl folk songs in close harmony or fell down a dry well in Corby and somehow survived for seven years by drinking rainwater and eating lichen and frogs, we'll never really know the truth of the matter. Of one thing we can be certain: when he appears on the radar again, his life begins its extraordinary upward trajectory.

This pattern is repeated with many other creative people. Little is known about Leonardo da Vinci for a period in his mid-thirties. Did he invent a helicopter powered by horse dung and fly it around the Tuscany region, as some claim? Or did he just take an extended beach holiday in Sicily, as others just as robustly postulate? Whatever the case, he came back so creatively hungry, as it were, that he painted *The Last Supper*.

Eastern mysticism has it that the Buddha disappeared for five years while he searched for the ultimate truth, during which he thought so hard that he attained enlightenment. He left society thin, long-haired and ignorant. He returned fat, bald and knowing everything. Apparently his wife hardly recognised him.

Let me make this clear: I do not put myself on the same level as Shakespeare, da Vinci or the Buddha. That would be astoundingly arrogant. But there is one thing I share with them and many other artists and thinkers: we all experienced times in our lives that were really bloody hard. Private times, largely unrecorded times, but, in the end, they were times that made us more whole. More real.

(Incidentally, while we're on the subject, there is even one man in Canada who argues ardently that Glen Miller did not really die in an aircraft over the English Channel in 1944 but went into hiding, and during the intervening, literally lost years he has been working obsessively on a new album of swing music, which he is planning to finally release in 2014 to coincide with his one hundred and tenth birthday.

Unlikely, I think, but stranger things have happened.)

I asked Paul about going back to live with his parents during those lost years.

PAUL: Well, of course, it was a hard time for me. I remember visiting them one Christmas, and my mum, bless her, was so upset at the state of me she made me stay for a few weeks. I was in no position to argue.

JOAN HAMILTON: Oh yes, he moved back in. For about a year in the end. I didn't mind, though. His father was less keen. But he really did need a bit of mothering. He had some sort of horrible rash when he first came back. Awful it was. Everywhere. I think he'd caught it off the sheets in one of the places he stayed at.

ERIC HAMILTON: You should have seen him. He looked like the elephant man. That Christmas, for a joke, I wrapped up a hood made out of a sack with one eye hole in it and gave it to him as a present. Thought it would cheer him up a bit. He didn't see the funny side, though. Stomped off upstairs in a right old tizz. Wouldn't even come down for his Christmas dinner. We had to leave it on a tray underneath the attic trapdoor. Got a proper earful from the missus for that one, dearie me.

But he was good for nothing while he was back. Did naff all. Just laid about watching telly and eating crisps.

PAUL: The stress had manifested itself as some kind of severe skin complaint. My theory is that I just felt so generally alienated that my body reacted accordingly, making me look physically 'other'. I certainly didn't feel as if I were living on the same planet as everyone else. I watched my *Man Who Fell to Earth* video a lot that year. I must certainly have given the impression that I was just being lazy, but all the time I was lying there I was in a state of deep contemplation. I began to see that I was at a very important crossroads. When I'd finally galvanised myself into realising that I had to go in a new direction, I saw that I didn't actually know which way to go. It could be this way. It could be that way. Or even a completely different way. Who knew? I certainly didn't. I had to take time to carefully, very carefully identify my options and then think those options through. But what were they? That was the first problem. I just did not know. But I was beginning to know that I would know. Some day.

ERIC HAMILTON: I kicked his bum out of the door in the end. I started thinking we'd never get rid of him. Remember *Sorry!*, that comedy programme on the telly with Ronnie Corbett? He's still living with his old mum at forty or something. I thought that was brilliant. Paul never wanted to watch it. But whenever it started I'd shout upstairs, 'Oi, come down here, you're on the telly!' So in the end I thought, 'Well, you've got to be a bit cruel to be kind, haven't you? Time to give him the heave-ho. He'll thank me for it in the end.' Besides, I wanted to use the attic for extra re-enactment space, as well as his old room, and I couldn't very well use it while he was still mooching around up there. It's not ideal trying to paint 500 American Civil War soldiers on the kitchen table when you've got the missus moaning about you getting under her feet! So in the end I bunged him a couple of hundred quid so he could set up a place back in London. That did the trick.

PAUL: I could have stayed, I guess. I could have thought to myself, 'Well, Paul, you tried to get out of Straightsville, but in the end the big bad world was just a little too big and a little too bad for you. Maybe you should get yourself a nice, quiet, ordinary job, find a nice, quiet, ordinary girl and have some nice, quiet, ordinary kids.' But I didn't. That seemed to be the loser's option. Having said that, let me quickly say this: if you're reading this and your job and your family are nice and quiet and ordinary, then please do be very proud of yourself. Sometimes I wish I could have settled for that. That wonderful simplicity. But I never could. I admire you. And I thank you. I thank you because the truth is we can't all go off on some crazy trajectory, spinning through the unchartered reaches of uncertainty, looking for God knows what and only knowing what it is when we find it, and even then not being quite sure whether it might be something else, or that it was in fact what we already had but we just didn't know it. If we all followed that crooked path instead of a more pedestrian one, well, then shirts would have no buttons, semi-skimmed milk would be unavailable, carpets would remain unfitted, broken toilets unmended, mouse infestations unpoisoned. And, quite frankly, I don't think I would want to live in a world like that.

And I don't believe you would either.

And so, in January 1990, after a pretty momentous decade that had lifted me up and then dashed me back down, I found myself battered but healing, older but still relatively young, cautious but defiant, and, incidentally, vegetarian (if occasionally eating chicken and ham). Here was a new decade, and I felt reborn. I was grateful to my folks for a brief shelter from the storm, but it wasn't too long before I was breaking it to them that I just had to move on again.

It was time to be dancing to a new tune.

16

ENTER SOPHIE MASTERSON

Sophie Masterson, then a thirty-five-year-old divorcee, had been renting a large room in a house in a leafy street in Belsize Park, North London, for some six months by the time Paul moved back to the capital.

Born the second daughter of the nineteenth Earl of Corby, she had grown up constantly rebelling against her aristocratic roots. At the age of seventeen she ran away with a woodworm specialist who had been working at her parents' stately home in Northamptonshire. She left him shortly after for his twin brother. By the time she was thirty she had married and divorced a telecoms engineer she met while he was sitting in a street testing wires, an ice-cream salesman, two of her psychotherapists and a male stripper called Marlon.

SOPHIE: Oh, I was a wild child from the off. I'm not exactly tame now – and I'm getting on a bit! Let's just say I've lived life to the full. Let me see, just off the top of my noddle, I've been arrested for weeing in Norman Tebbit's petrol tank – that took some aiming – I've been knocked out by an ostrich, lived up a tree for six weeks with an Indonesian witch doctor, worked on a telephone sex line – 'Posh Pam, have one off the aristo' (I thought of that) – oh, and I once killed an Alsatian with my bare hands. Had to. It was coming for me. I've cleaned windows, stalked

Jeremy Clarkson and swum Lake Windermere in a wedding dress (last-minute wobble). I've even been exorcised. Apparently I was possessed for a few weeks by a demon called Tharallax. You should be writing a book about me!

On the day he moved back to London, sitting in a greasy spoon in Soho, suitcase by his feet, Paul struck lucky. Scouring the accommodation ads in the ever-reliable small-ads paper *Loot*, he picked out a room for rent, called the number and arranged to view it that very evening.

PAUL: One of the two women living in the house showed me around. She was quite drunk but very pleasant. An infant-school teacher. I was offered the room on the spot. She told me the other tenant was currently away in Germany on a sausage-tasting holiday. I thought no more about it.

The tenant in question who was away sampling Bratwurst was none other than Sophie Masterson. I asked Paul about how they got together.

PAUL: Well, it wasn't exactly love at first sight for me, I have to say. But let me backtrack a little. I'd actually been pretty unlucky in the romance department. That is, until I met Sophie, of course. I had a steady girlfriend when I was fifteen. We saw each other for over a year, but then she decided she was gay. I was pretty upset at the time but, hey, she found her niche, and that's what's important. Then there was another girl I was pretty heavily into while I was working at Boldgate Windows. She turned out to be gay too. And when a girl I met at a Thompson Twins gig who I was on the point of moving in with revealed she was gay too, I nearly freaked. I secretly started calling myself 'the Lesbianator'. The point is, these experiences had given me some quite severe trust issues. In that I couldn't trust that any woman I formed a relationship with wouldn't at some point announce that there was someone else, and that the someone else in question was someone else who urinated whilst sitting down. There had been plenty of one-night stands over the years, but as I entered my thirties I started limiting them. There's often a feeling of revulsion and disgust that follows the casual encounter that simply can't be hidden. It's a common experience, but after a while I couldn't help but take it personally. So when I met Sophie I never dreamed that we'd end up together. For a start – and I know she won't be offended – she's actually quite manly looking. She's three inches taller than me for a start. And she's one strong lady. When she shakes your hand, your hand knows it's been shaken. My immediate impression was that she was of the sapphic persuasion. How wrong I was. Shallow prejudice on my part, for which I ought to be ashamed. And am.

Sophie, however, was immediately entranced by Paul.

SOPHIE: Oh gosh, he's always just been catnip to me. It's ludicrous. God knows why. He's not particularly good-looking, is he? He can bore for England, if you let him. And he's so moody! But almost the moment I saw him . . .

I mean, something just went badoing! It's just too weird. I remember thinking, 'Oh gosh, I'm having you, you funny little man. You're mine!'

PAUL: I had no idea. No idea at all. Looking back now, it was obvious. She was always coming into my room. Quite often she wouldn't be wearing much. I just thought she felt comfortable in my presence. It was when she came in wearing nothing at all that I thought, 'Now hang on.'

SOPHIE: Yes, I had to sort of dish it out to him. He didn't really seem to be picking up any of the signals. And I wasn't exactly being subtle. I was always saying the most ridiculously fruity things, lolling all over his bed, playing with my hair, sucking my fingers, tra la la. I had to literally pin him down in the end. Came in one night after quite a few voddies with the girls and dived on him. I thought he was going to have a heart attack. Apparently he'd thought I was a lezzer! Silly so-and-so. I mean, I did give the old girl-on-girl a whirl once just to see what all the fuss was about. Quite good fun actually, but it wasn't really the ticket for me. When it comes down to it, there's no escaping it: I really do appreciate a chap's chap.

PAUL: She left me in no doubt about her feelings, and at first I wasn't sure how to react. I mean, she's everything I thought I wouldn't want. She's not particularly ladylike. Now I know that sounds sexist, but I've seen her punch a mugger so hard on the back of the head that he tried to sue her for bruising his brain. And if Chelsea lose a match, it's as well to stay out of her way. Having said that, she'll cry like a baby if I buy her a cuddly toy, and she spends a fortune on bras. But her background is completely alien to me. It's a world I'd only caught a glimpse of in films and books. The first time she took me to meet her parents, they wanted me to go out and shoot things with them. There's a fountain in their library, for God's sake! Let's just say, there's a little bit of a culture gap there.

SOPHIE: Paul's only been home with me a few times. Mummy thinks he's quite sweet, but Daddy thinks he's a bit of a drip. But that's Daddy for you. I knew there'd be a bit of a scene if the chat got round to politics and, of course, first time we were there, a few bottles of Beaujolais in and it all kicked off. Daddy's quite a bigwig in UKIP – soooo embarrassing – and he started getting on his high horse about the Bulgarians. Again. I thought, 'Oh, Lord, here we go.' Paul started sticking up for them, but he didn't do a very good job. He doesn't know a thing about Bulgaria. Well, I mean, who does? All I know is that they wear clogs. Then we got onto class, and Paul made a complete ninny of himself getting our butler Dudderidge to sit in his seat while Paul poured him a glass of vino. He was so sozzled he spilt most of it down poor old Duddy's shirt. Mummy and I were in hysterics, but Daddy and Paul both got themselves worked up into a complete lather. Men are so silly, aren't they? It was even worse the next time we went. Daddy ended up chasing him around the house with a cutlass my great-grandfather used on the last ever cavalry charge in the First World War. Complete disaster. As I say, though, Mummy's a lot less anti. Actually, more than anything she's probs just glad I broke it off with the mercenary I was engaged to. Even Daddy was a little bit scared of him.

Paul admits that Sophie made an immediate impact on his life in a number of ways.

PAUL: Oh, totally, yes. I stopped eating boil-in-the-bag meals for a start. And she got me into rap in quite a big way. That's been very significant, in fact. If you listen carefully, you can hear the influence of rap very clearly in a lot of my work.

But Sophie was to make a major impact on his life, changing it for ever when, on Tuesday 15 May 1990, she suggested they go and meet a friend of hers who was appearing at a poetry club.

17

JUSTIN WIVERLY

Sophie had been friends for many years with a poet called Justin Wiverly. They'd met in their early teens at a Christmas ball given by Sophie's parents, immediately hitting it off after getting totally blotto on a stolen bottle of cherry brandy and throwing figgy pudding at an elderly duchess. Justin's father was a bishop, and his land backed onto that of Sophie's parents. Like Sophie, Justin was at odds with his toff upbringing and had 'gone off the rails', as his father put it, at an early age.

Justin's brother, Donald, an assistant dean at Salisbury Cathedral, takes up the story.

DONALD WIVERLY: People often marvelled at how very different Justin and I were. I was always the quiet, studious one and just got on with things. Justin was a different sort entirely. I think Mother and Father began to worry after he was sent home from nursery for eating the class stick insect. He always was a very troubled person. Throughout his childhood he was analysed, therapised, evaluated and put on various types of medication. They tried absolutely everything. Mother, much against Father's wishes, even resorted to sending him to India to meet a famous guru-type lady said to be possessed of divine powers. A light kiss from this woman bestowed upon the top of one's head was supposed to bring tranquillity and happiness to a troubled soul. Justin nearly caused a diplomatic incident by returning the kiss in the 'French' style, whilst massaging her buttocks with both hands. It was so very distressing for us all. It cost the family a considerable amount of time and effort to make that go away. And then, finally, after much agonising, Father sent Justin, who was now in his late teens, to two corrective establishments designed to deliver the so-called 'short, sharp shock' treatment. In the first place he sparked a riot, causing a quarter of a million pounds' worth of damage, and in the next he was sent home and labelled as 'unreformable' after being caught in flagrante with the facility matron in a wheelie bin. My parents were in despair.

Nothing could tame him. Justin Wiverly was a whirlwind, a bundle of manic energy causing havoc wherever he went. By his late teens he had taken every possible psychedelic and amphetamine-based concoction he could get his hands on. By his early twenties he was seriously addicted to heroin. After, being sent to jail for attempting to sell his father's mitre and crook for drug money he emerged from prison a year later declaring himself 'Bored of narcotics'. Now, in his mid-thirties, he had settled on massive daily intakes of booze as his preferred means of stimulation.

Justin had always seen himself as a poet, and, indeed, by his mid-twenties had achieved cult status on the poetry-reading circuit. A collection of his poetry entitled *Turds* had attracted a small but fanatical group of devotees. This was available as a bundle of sheets of A4 paper roughly stapled together by Justin himself, which he sold at his gigs for fifty pence each. The poems had been photocopied onto these creased or torn bits of paper, which were often stained with food, blood and other matter perhaps best left not too closely examined. The pages of the longer poems were often stuck together in the wrong order, and this stirred up heated debate among his hundred or so diehard fans as to which versions were the best, or 'real', ones.

The night Paul Hamilton first encountered Justin Wiverly was to be the night his eyes were opened to a whole new world. Paul remembers initially feeling far from enthusiastic about the prospect of having to go and watch a bunch of poets reading out their work in a back room somewhere in Clapham.

PAUL: I wasn't keen, I really wasn't. Sophie's taken me to some awful places over the years: a human dissection, a bare-knuckle fight in a warehouse, an audience with Peter Hitchens. There are others too unsettling to mention. She does have a taste for the bizarre. I was aware within a couple of months of knowing her that 'a night out' was something of a lottery. So when she said she'd arranged to see a couple of her friends at a poetry night, alarm bells started ringing. But, as ever, Sophie was insistent. And I have to say, I'm so very glad she was. This was to be a huge turning point in my life, and by association, I suppose, the life of anybody who's ever got into my work. It was to be the night I realised what I wanted to be. A poet.

SOPHIE: He didn't want to go, but I knew he'd love it so I made him. Ended up dragging him out of the house by his hair.

'Poetry at the Plough' was a monthly poetry night run by Sophie's friend Charmian Mason in a tiny room above a pub. Sophie and Paul arrived to find the venue nearly empty. Charmian explained to them that earlier there'd been about sixty people in but when she'd announced that Justin Wiverly had called at the last moment to cancel his appearance, all but a handful of the gathered poetry fans had immediately asked for their money back and left.

PAUL: It seemed the star attraction wasn't going to show. I was all for leaving and taking in a Rossellini at the Screen on the Green, but Sophie knew one or two of the other poets on the bill and suggested that as we'd come this far, we might as well stay. I settled down for what I thought was going to be a dreary evening. The club organiser opened the proceedings with some of her own material. She immediately captured my imagination. It was pretty heavy stuff. There was one about ovarian cysts; another about her brother who'd been electrocuted to death by his train set. And I remember a very graphic piece that imagined Paul Raymond raping himself with his own penis. It was all very unsettling, but, I have to say, I was transfixed. It seemed so uncompromising, and that impressed me. I thought back to Valerie, the 'poet' whom I had encountered at the polytechnic. There was that same level of unhinged fury at work in Charmian, but there was some other, extra element which was nothing short of spell-binding. I don't know what it was. Sometimes the difference between poetry that demands your attention and mere screeching in the wind is something that defies description.

SOPHIE: Paul's a boobs man. Through and through. So I always knew he was going to appreciate Charmian. And, of course, he did. And she never was one for bras. His tongue was practically on the floor! She could have been reading the telephone book for all he'd've cared.

PAUL: The other poets were all intriguing in their own ways. A small, nervous woman performed a fairly long piece which I thought was some kind of Dadaist soundscape. It was Sophie who pointed out that in fact she had a very bad stammer. Fascinating, nonetheless. A mature lady regaled us with some very heartfelt poems about her self-loathing. And a Welsh guy with a very quiet voice half whispered some poems, and although you couldn't actually hear them, you could tell from the expressions on his face that whatever he was saying, he really meant it. It was the contrast that got me: whether it was the haunted youth all in black with his five-minute poem in which he repeated the word 'death' with ever greater intensity and emotion, or the cheerful pensioner comically bemoaning his fading ability to achieve tumescence, they all spoke to me in one way or another. And as the beer flowed so did the words and rhythms of this eclectic bunch of endearing individuals. Amusing, challenging, heartbreaking, horrifying and uplifting – it was wonderful.

There was a break, and as we ordered more drinks downstairs, Charmian spoke with Sophie, fretting that Justin Wiverly's no-show was going to necessitate her filling in time by letting her boyfriend do some of his poetry. This wasn't ideal as, apparently, he'd written a twenty-minute piece on the decline of socialism, and it was very much a

'first draft'. Half an hour later we were all back upstairs in
our seats and Charmian's boyfriend was in the middle of a
torturous metaphor involving the Aids virus and the concept of the closed shop. Just as I was about to lose the fight
to not bury my face in my hands, a slurred voice rang out
from the door: 'Who wants to hear some fucking real poetry?' Stumbling through the chairs, spilling several drinks
– two of them his own – a startling figure lurched into
the performance area. As he narrowly avoided knocking
Charmian into some boxes of lemon Scampi Fries, whilst
actually sending her boyfriend flying into a broken kara-
oke machine, I rose to my feet. My first thought was that
this was one of the rowdier element from the saloon bar,
come to cause trouble. I was all ready to run downstairs
and call the police when Charmian cried out, 'Justin, you
drunken bastard!' And there he stood, swaying slightly,
breathing heavily. Justin Wiverly. On a whim he'd decided
to show up after all. Or he had forgotten he had cancelled.
Or he had cancelled to amuse himself and then turned
up out of sheer bloody-minded devilment. Unshaven, his
black hair a wild mess, his bottle-green velvet suit faded
and threadbare, his frilly white shirt stained with traces
of unidentifiable liquids and foodstuffs, his Cuban-heeled
shoes scuffed and mud-spattered, he presented an extraordinary vision. A nervous titter from the audience elicited
a sharp 'Shut your cock!', after which his eyes rolled into
the back of his head and there, in the middle of us all, he
began.

It is impossible to evoke what the experience of witness-
ing a live reading by Justin was like. That night he ranged

through several of the poems from his self-published collection of poetry, *Turds*. I've since read and re-read my copy of *Turds* many times, battered and faded though it is. On a low night, or maybe after a few too many whiskies, I can become incandescent with rage that it was never taken up by any of the big poetry publishers. Shame on them. And, yes, that includes you, Faber & Faber.

Turds on paper is pretty overpowering. *Turds* from the author's own mouth was beyond belief. A scattergun volley of semi-abstract word-mix, I was assailed by nightmarish imagery that occasionally made me doubt my ears, my very sanity. It was a tsunami of dredged-up psychoses and tamped-down phobiae, insistent, obsessive, shattering and really, really bloody rude. All delivered with an accompaniment of a deluge of saliva, a shower of mucus and lashings of sweat, his arms flailing, his eyes rolling, his voice a cracked shriek. Here's an extract from a piece he delivered that night called 'Emergency Number Four':

> *Slapped gorilla bleeding from the ears, gently placed up-*
> *   right in the burnt-out Mazda.*
> *Well, you surprised us there, you spartan little fetcher of pus.*
> *But!*
> *Beware the dead man's fart, secretly circulating, penetrating,*
> *defining the very essence of your tom-tit tedious magazine-*
> *   demise and meanwhile,*
> *meanwhile,*
> *meanwhile, as I spunk my fate all over God's dreaming face*
> *   (oh, Dresden!) I think of you:*
> *sixpence in silver foil,*

salted slugs for fingers,
worse than any fucking cat.

Ladies and gentlemen: poetry.

Most of the small crowd, none of them Wiverly fans, had walked out by the time he'd finished (or, rather, keeled over, banging his head quite nastily on a fuse box). As the evening came to this typically Wiverlian end, there was only Sophie, myself and Charmian left, her boyfriend having exited in high dudgeon after his undignified forced exit from the spotlight.

I was speechless. As Charmian and Sophie rolled him into the recovery position and applied ice to the swelling lump at the back of his head, I could only sit and stare. I knew at that very moment that I wanted to make that kind of imprint, that kind of mark, because that is what he had done: Justin Claudius Hannibal Wiverly had come into that room that night and made a deep, deep impression on me. Deeper even than the one he had made on the fuse box!

After dropping Justin off at his digs in a rather run-down part of Kentish Town, we took the taxi back to Belsize Park. And, as the city night passed its ever-moving orange hues over us, I heard myself whispering to my now drowsy lover, 'Sophie, I am going to be a poet.'

Her reply, though unworded, could have been taken to be not exactly encouraging, but it did not matter. I knew. I just knew.

18

THE CHRYSALIS CRACKS

PAUL: After my first encounter with Justin, my immediate reaction was that I wanted to talk to this remarkable character, to get some tips, find out how his mind worked.

It was to prove difficult.

I persuaded Sophie to take me to the next three readings Justin was giving. At the first one he was attacked by the boyfriend of a woman in the audience after sticking his head up her skirt. He ended up in casualty with concussion. The second time we went to see him was on a stiflingly hot summer's night. Justin, in the excitement of his performance, managed to totter backwards and through the open window behind him, luckily for him falling from the first floor onto a hen party in the street below. On the third occasion the owner of the poetry club made an offhand comment about Justin's handkerchief, which resulted in a tirade of such exceptional rage that I thought he might actually explode, after which he succumbed to torrents of tears. Utterly inconsolable, he came home with us that night, and after he had drunk every last drop of alcohol in the house – including an entire bottle of advocaat he'd insisted through his tears on buying from an off-licence en route – he went to sleep on the settee.

The next morning – or, rather, afternoon – I took him tea and toast. As he had not moved by early evening, I took him some more tea and sat down. I had to try to get to know him, find out what made him tick. Shyly but frankly, I spoke at some length about my admiration for his passion and artistry. I confessed to him that I felt more inspired than I ever had about anything and that, because of him, I wanted to be a poet. When I finished there was a long silence. I didn't dare to look at him. Then I heard him say, very distinctly and very slowly, 'Is it time for *Coronation Street* yet?' I didn't understand. I was at a loss as to how I should reply. Was this a line from one of his poems? Was he making a statement about artifice posing as reality? Was it some kind of test?

He did in fact want to know if it was time for *Coronation Street*. I knew that it was going to be very difficult to get this enigmatic guy to open up, but I was determined to persevere. The first thing I wanted to do was to show Justin some of the song lyrics I had written during my time with Charlie. Just for some feedback, a little guidance.

If I ever see a poet who's just starting out, or even one who's been going for a while, I won't hesitate to give them a few markers: there's a little bit too much of this, not enough of that, have you thought about such and such . . . whatever I think may help. I know that many are just too shy or insecure to ask me what I think, so it's a pleasure to be able to put them out of their misery. Sometimes you have to be direct. Occasionally unwelcomingly so. That doesn't always elicit smiling gratitude exactly, but in the long run, after my feedback has been ingested, I hope it proves of some use. With regard to trying to get some reaction from Justin, the results were not encouraging. Invariably I would hand my lyrics over when he was drunk, and he would then either lose them or forget all about them. One morning, when we'd once again put him up at our digs after he had inadvertently set fire to his lodgings during an absinthe session, we'd been woken by terrifying howls of rage and despair. We rushed in to find him kneeling on the floor with the lyrics I had written in his shaking hands. Eventually we got it out of him that he thought he had written them whilst inebriated (in which state, needless to say, he wrote most of his work) and that he had finally, irrevocably 'lost his mojo'. When I sheepishly explained that it was my work he was clutching, his reaction was to freeze and then bury his face in the sheets and rock backwards and forwards for a very long time, moaning, 'Oh, thank God, thank God, thank God.' My humiliation was complete.

SOPHIE: I told Paul that if he wanted to write poetry, he should start by reading some to see how it was done. I told him that song lyrics were a different cut of meat all together. He'd read some out to me, you see, and they were mostly a bit of a yawn. There was one called 'Your Plastic World'. It went something like: 'I've been round and round and round and round and round and round and round and round and round and round, all around, around your plastic world.' He told me to be honest about what I thought. So I told him it made me feel a bit queasy. He went into a massive sulk about that and stormed off. Didn't see him for hours. When he came back, I couldn't get a peep out of him. I said, 'Why aren't you talking to me?' He said, 'Oh, I didn't want to make you feel queasy, that's all.' Well, he got a jolly hard slap for that. Thing is, you might as well be frank in these cases, don't you think? No point in beating about the bush. I had a chum who wanted to be an artist, and she wasted years painting these simply awful blobs. That's all she did, paint blobs. Blue blobs. Red blobs. Yellow blobs. Sometimes just one blob. Sometimes hundreds of the horrid things. Whenever she showed me one of her blob pictures, I'd always say something neutral. You know, 'Oh, an orange blob.' Or, 'That's a big blob.' In the end she asked me what I actually thought of them. 'Of your blobs?' I said. 'Nothing. They're coloured blobs. What am I supposed to think of them, you silly goose?' And she said, 'Yes, they're a bit boring, aren't they?' And I said, 'Boring? They're beyond tedious. I'm sick of the sight of your blobs, now that you ask.' And she said, 'You know what, Sophes? You're right. You should have said. I'm going to stop painting blobs now and move on to something else.' So she did. Went and did a degree in mechanical engineering. Now, if I'd told her straight off about the blobs, she'd've spent more time doing something useful like . . . gosh, I don't know, designing kinematic chains or something instead of wasting all those years painting thousands of silly, boring, pointless coloured blobs. I thought, 'Well, I'll never make that mistake again.'

PAUL: I showed Sophie some of the lyrics I'd written. I needed to get a second opinion. Were they really as bad as Justin had made out? She was very supportive and found some positive things to say, but I knew something wasn't right. I thought long and hard, and I remember suddenly realising in a moment of intense clarity that it was the fact these were song lyrics that was the problem. I needed to start writing poetry. Lyrics weren't the same thing. And I was right. A lyric is always accompanied by its friend the song. The song is there to support it, to strengthen it, to beautify it. A poem on the other hand is a lonesome thing and has no access to such flattery. So it had better be saying something worth listening to. There is a very great difference and, for the most part, that difference is a matter of quality. I put it to you: Armitage or Blunt? Whose words would you have tattooed on your face?

To write poetry, and really great poetry at that, I knew that it had to come from me. From my life. When I told Sophie this she suggested I start reading all the greats – Tennyson, Manley Hopkins, Plath, Eliot, those kinds of guys – and she was very shocked when I told her I would not. The reason was simple: for the first time in my life I needed to find my own voice. Looking at my song lyrics I realised that all I had been doing was aping Lennon, parodying Weller, mimicking Sayer. Sure, I was producing reasonable pastiches, but they weren't the real deal. I knew that if I was to become a truly original poet I was going to have to keep my channels pure and, in order to do so, I was, due to a higher calling I could not ignore, going to have to deny myself the joy of the poetry of others. I'm proud to say that as a poet I have hardly read or listened to any other great poets' works. Whenever I reveal this fact, it really floors a lot of people, but that pride is, of course, tempered with a great sadness. I simply daren't risk compromising my own style. I must banish the sublime. I have only to listen to one or two poems of a poet to determine whether that poet's work is to be forever excised from my life or not. (If, however, a poet's work is, in my opinion, unexceptional then I will greedily ingest it, sincerely grateful to that poet for the opportunity to learn how *not* to go about things). All in all though, my self-denial is a bitter, bitter part of what is mostly the wonderful privilege of being a poet. I have wept at the thought that I will never fully savour the Scouse drollery of McGough, the suburban charm of Betjeman, the rootsy verbal ragga of Kwesi Johnson or the ghostly voice of Owen. But I can't let them in. I must keep them out.

Over the years I have had to go to extraordinary lengths not to listen to other people's poetry. If I am in someone else's car and some laudable poetry comes on the radio, then I will not, of course, impose my moratorium on the car owner because this is my own particular cross to bear. I will, in fact, urge them to listen, and then stick my head out of the car window. (This happened some years ago on a short tour of the Scottish Highlands in the depths of winter and, as a result, I went on to suffer frostbite on the end of my nose. The plus side was that I became acutely aware that two of my fillings needed attention.) I know that I am denying myself great art, but it is the only way I can retain my authenticity. This is so important to me, and I believe it's important to the folk who enjoy my work. And to prove the point: I was once suffering a vicious bout of flu and had been watching television from my sick bed. A programme about Ogden Nash came on. Unable to find the remote control, and too weak to move or shout over the TV, I was forced to watch the whole hour-long documentary. Now Nash is more than a little lightweight for my liking but, even so, he is a strong fla-vour and, as a result of that unwilling exposure, for the next six months I could not write a single poem without it sounding like a piece of light whimsy. I kept one that I wrote on learning that the father of an old friend had died when he stepped in front of an express train:

> Poor old Mister Hobbs,
> Life did not meet his needs.
> So instead he met a choo-choo which was
> Bound for Temple Meads.

You see my point. I could hardly have written that on the card I sent with the wreath.

And so, having ceremoniously burned all my old song lyrics one night at the top of Primrose Hill, I bought myself a brand-new notebook and set of HBs and took my first baby steps towards discovering my own poeti-cal identity. But there was trouble yet ahead. Despite my sincere resolution to create an entirely new wordscape, I had vastly underestimated the powerful gravitational pull of the Wiverlian influence. Every single one of those first callow, naïve attempts at poems were, in the crassest fashion, Wiverly-lite. They were Shaking Stevens to Elvis Presley, Jilly Cooper to Virginia Woolf, Darren Bett to Mi-chael Fish. And the laughable thing is, I myself was totally and utterly unaware that I was churning out nothing but crude, hollow impersonations.

Looking back at those pieces, I see that where Justin had

written a piece called 'Zoo Bomb', I'd come up with 'Safari Detonation'; in answer to his 'There's an Octopus in My Bottom Hole', I had subconsciously replied with 'Squid Balls'; and having ingested his 'Gulf Warhol', I'd sweated out 'Apartheid of Rudeness'.

It was, of course, Justin himself who taught me the error of my poetical ways. It wasn't what you'd call a gentle lesson. He had broken his foot kicking a wall because he couldn't think of a satisfactory rhyme for 'insipid', and was laid up – again – at ours. Seeing that I had him captive, as it were, I laid my offerings by the settee while he was dozing and then retired. After two days of waiting for some comment I timidly asked him if he had read my poems. He was very calm. He said he had. Silence. I asked him what he thought of them. Silence. I was about to leave the room when he began: a slow, deliberate stream of some of the most shattering sentences I have ever heard in the English language. Sentences delivered without pause, totally coherent, terrible in their beauty, beautiful in their terribleness. I have cursed a thousand times my inability to remember what he said in those next ten minutes or so, damned my total ineptitude in not discreetly flicking my portable Dictaphone on and committing it all to posterity. Mind you, if I had, I'm not so sure I'd have ever had the courage to play it back. As his eviscerating monologue ground mercilessly on I remember his eyes remained permanently fixed on the television, on which *Bullseye* was playing out its saloon-bar pantomime. Coldly, dispassionately, he set about tearing apart what I had written, verse by verse, sentence by sentence, word by word, syllable by syllable. He viciously dissected my punctuation errors, even spending five minutes eloquently disparaging the particular shade of ink I had written my poems in. It was like being slowly immersed in acid. When he had finished he held the bits of paper out and, without looking at me, said, 'Would you like them back?'

I remember taking them and stupidly thanking him, and then walking out and going to my room. I have never cried very easily, but the tears flowed without cease that evening. I was still weeping when Sophie came back from paintballing and asked me what on earth was wrong. When I told her, she laughed and said she'd only just been talking to Justin about my poems, and he'd said that although he had many points of criticism (didn't I know it!), there were one or two that 'showed a glimmer'. I was flabbergasted. The main note, apparently, was that I had no voice of my own. I'd certainly picked that up from the tirade downstairs earlier. He had got that across very clearly – including, with regard to my slavish copyings of his style, accusing me of (and this is the one sentence from that searing onslaught that remains in my memory intact) 'sucking his juice out like a King's Cross rent boy and then shitting it onto a girl's notebook'.

I thank Justin Wiverly every day for what I now realise was a great act of compassion. Without that big-hearted critique of my first floundering attempts at writing poetry maybe I would never have taken it quite so seriously. Perhaps I would have been doomed to an even more hideous fate than being a bad poet: being a mediocre one.

19

CRITICS

Paul claims that his early exposure to Justin Wiverly's forth-right reactions to his poetry has made him entirely indifferent to the opinions of professional critics.

PAUL: They simply don't register.

Over the years Paul has received many reviews from poetry magazines and, later, online poetry websites. Sophie has always made a point of faithfully collecting anything that is written or said about Paul's work.

SOPHIE: Well, it's always jolly interesting to read the different reactions to Paul's poems. Sometimes you wonder if they're talking about the same man. Paul says he never reads them, but he does. I keep the magazine reviews in a drawer, and years ago I started doing that thing where you sellotape a hair across the side of the drawer – you know the one – so that when the drawer is opened it pulls the hair loose and you know someone's been in there. Learned that at boarding school. A horrid little stinker called Mary Swift had been telling all these filthy stories about me and boys from the academy up the road. All true, of course. But she could only have known by sneaking a peek at my diary. So I put a bogus entry in about me and the sixth-form rugby team and put the diary in my bedside drawer, to which I then attached a hair. Next morning I noticed the hair was unstuck, and by lunchtime the rugby rumour was all round the school. All I can say is that after prep that evening so were her teeth. I hear she's a marriage guidance counsellor now. The mind boggles. But anyway, whenever I file a new review, Paul will always steal a sly look. I can tell because, if it's a good one, he starts humming silly, jaunty tunes. Just hums all around the flat. For a good couple of hours. But if it's a bad one, he either goes quiet or turns on the radio or television and shouts at it. He'll deny it, of course, but the hair never lies!

PAUL: No, I don't read my reviews and I never will. I can understand, though, you telling me that they're very different. I think more interesting, challenging art tends to polarise opinion. There's a French artist, Georges Boulangier, who works with sheep's eyes. Coats them with a clear preservative and then sticks them all over household objects – Hoovers, saucepans and so on. Fraud or genius? Thing is, he's selling these things for tens of thousands. President Obama has one on his desk in the Whitehouse. Brian Sewell called the same guy 'a dirty little phoney it's almost worth rebuilding the Bastille for'. The point is, he's started a debate, and that's got to be a good thing. Hasn't it? What about Joshua Silberstein, the Israeli situationist? Covers his boiler suit with industrial-strength adhesive and then attaches himself halfway up world-famous monuments. The Statue of Liberty, the Taj Mahal, Nelson's Column, there's no major place of interest he hasn't stuck himself to and been cut down from. They used a taser to knock him off Abraham Lincoln. Genius or fraud? To his supporters he's a visionary who engages with an object originally conceived to express some meaningful aspect of humanity which, due to overfamiliarity, has become something merely physical, and he subverts the perceived inanimation of that object and rehumanises it by literally becoming a part of it on behalf of all of us. And yet to his detractors he's just 'the Gloonatic'.

I asked Paul if he would just for once break with his refusal to read any of his reviews and let me show him two that really sum up the division in opinion over his poetry. I was surprised and pleased when he agreed. First I showed him a favourable review from a 1997 edition of the now defunct free poetry magazine *Line Beats*, which was available three times a year in libraries in Suffolk. The review, written by the magazine's editor and sole contributor, Nicola Hurst, offers thoughts on a reading Paul did at the Durham Arts Centre in May of that year.

And so to the best poet of the evening by far, Mister Paul Hamilton. And incidentally, look out for an exclusive interview with the Man Himself in the next issue, issue 35 of Line Beats. *For previous interviews please refer to issues 12, 15, 18, 22, 27, 30 and 31. Tonight, as always, Paul does not disapoint [sic]. All of our old favourites are there and special praise must be given to his reading of 'Africa', where Paul inhabits the persona of an African driven to hatred by centuries of oppression and exploitation and, while beating a small drum in time to his voice, scarily intones the chilling manntra [sic] 'Kill the white man, kill the white* man, kill the white man, kill the white man'. Of the one hundred and twenty-four poetry readings by Paul that I have attended I have no problem in rating this as the fourteenth best ever. It was not quite as good as his reading at the Havant Literary Festival on March 19th 1995, but it is nevertheless a bit better than his July 10th 1996 reading at the Shrewsbury Arts Festival. The Shrewsbury Arts Festival reading, very good though it was, must now be demoted to fifteenth best ever poetry reading by Paul that I have attended.

The most exciting part of tonight's experience is the totally unexpected bonus of an entirely new poem!

The heartbreaking 'Ring' begins simply with the word 'ring' repeated in the rhythm of the famous melody line to Mendelson's [sic] 'Wedding March'. The poem then conjures up the sad solitude of an evening spent by a man at home alone after he can't bring himself to go to an old flame's wedding. The entire poem is reproduced here from the recording I made of the performance. Please do not read this without first listening to the 'Wedding March' if you do not already know it.

RING

Ring ring ring ring ring ring ring
Ring ring ring ring ring ring
Ring out the bells.
Ring out the hankies.
I'll ring out for pizza.
Ring ring

Ring ring
Ring ring.
They must be busy.
Ring ring
Ring ring.
Well, it is a Saturday night.
Ring ring.
I will call back later.
Ring.
I. Will.

By the time he reached the end of his set Paul was sweating and so was I! A fantastic effort from Paul. Well done, Paul, and I hope you enjoyed my cake!

After this I showed Paul a review from Hugh Spencer of *The Cambridge Versifier*, who had seen him reading his work at 'The Train of Poetry', a regular poetry night in Cambridge, in September 2006.

Finally, to end the evening, what a treat: a poet of magnificent subtlety, imagination and wit. But just before her: Paul Hamilton.

PAUL: Is that it? Right. Well, there you go. Perfect example. There's that polarisation thing I was talking about. I'd rather not dwell too much on the first one, flattering though it is. Let's just say that the relationship between that particular critic and my work became a little too personal. It pains me to say it but sometimes there really is no alternative other than to call the police.

As for the second review. Well. God, it breaks my heart when someone tries to write poetry, fails and then tries to take his revenge by becoming a critic. And I bet you that's what happened with poor old Hugh. It's a very common phenomenon. That guy has always been relentlessly negative about my work and, as you can see, pretty damn rude. But I guess if you have low self-esteem and you've lost your hair pretty early on and you're struggling with your weight, you may end up resorting to that kind of behaviour. It's sad if you do, but entirely understandable. I bear no malice. I just hope that some day the guy lets go of all that poison and finds some kind of peace.

20

NO MORE, NO MORE

Paul considers Justin Wiverly's death to be one of the saddest events in his life, despite the fact that it came as no surprise to anybody.

DONALD WIVERLY: Justin spent his whole life in the shadow of Death. His health was poor from the day he was born. Within the first month of his life he suffered measles, chicken pox and malaria. Our nanny was a great traditionalist and insisted that the window of our nursery remain open every night of the year. Consequently, by the time he was three he had contracted pneumonia twice and had developed a morbid fear of owls, a fear which later turned into a pathological hatred. Scarlet fever, tuberculosis and scrofula all plagued his pre-pubescence. Sadly, drug abuse later added hepatitis A, B, C and D to the list of woes, on top of which his frankly cavalier attitude towards personal hygiene inevitably led to a constant stream of various fungal infections, impacted hairs and dental abscesses.

It was, in fact, Justin's childhood terror of owls that finally did for him.

In the summer of 1991 he embarked on what was even for him an eye-poppingly excessive binge that lasted more or less without break from Thursday 6 June until Monday 18 September. By the end of this mammoth session he had exhausted every last source of credit, got himself arrested six times, estranged himself from most of his friends for ever and had had the word 'shit' tattooed across his face. After he was dropped off at his parents' house by Sophie, they immediately called in doctors from Harley Street and he was installed in his old nursery under heavy sedation.

DONALD WIVERLY: It was all terribly sad. For a few weeks we actually thought he was getting better. But then one night in early October Julian was woken by the sound of an owl hooting somewhere in the grounds. This, of course, would have thrown him into a blind rage. Unfortunately, our parents were in London at the time. The staff had been given strict instructions to keep a watchful eye on him, but he'd dismissed them all in his usual robust manner, so there was no one around to calm him down. The coroner's report eventually offered the scenario that in a confused and agitated state, probably not helped by the alcohol which he had ingested via several bottles of mouthwash, he had staggered into the night, still in his pyjamas, to try to silence the hooting owl. He was seen from the house the next day lying under a large oak tree. The servants assumed that he was sleeping off the effects of another one of his 'big nights'. They were only too aware of the awful consequences of attempting to awaken him after such an event. I myself once tried and, although he did get out of bed, it was only to pick it up and throw it at me. Poor Justin lay under that tree for half the night and most of the next day before one of the gardeners cautiously approached him to shoo away a squirrel, only to discover that my poor brother was nearly comatose, with a very weak pulse.

Justin was taken to hospital, but it was too late. On hearing the terrible news Sophie and Paul rushed to his bedside and were able to say their goodbyes before he slipped away.

PAUL: I still can't talk about it. I'm just so honoured that, along with his family, I was there when he passed away. He rallied a little just before he died, so I'm glad he knew that I was there. I can't really add anything to the poem that I wrote about him, 'Tribute to Justin Wiverly' (see page 233). I'll always be grateful to him. I learned so much. His advice, for example, not to think too much during the process of creating original poetry. Justin caught me thinking once. He asked me if I'd swallowed some bleach. Typical Justin. I told him I was trying to write poetry. He taught me a very valuable thing that day: he said that you do not make poetry happen, poetry happens of its own accord – 'like a boil on your arse', as he put it. I realised then that I had to be a bit more relaxed. In fact, I became a bit too relaxed, because three months later I suddenly realised that not only had I not written any poetry, but I'd stopped even thinking about being a poet and, indeed, had started to consider opening a Filofax shop. I'd over-redressed the balance. I had to find the middle way, and that's exactly what I did and still do to this day. I think very hard about poetry on alternate days. In the days in between I just let my mind idle completely. It's a happy medium.

To me, Justin was a hero I could not help but worship. He could be very cruel and, gosh, he had a kick like a mule, but his energy and passion and sheer inventiveness were as addictive as the crack cocaine he so completely doted on until his third heart attack. When he wasn't around, the world became a rainy Sunday afternoon in 1971 at your great-auntie Ivy's semi-detached in Tunbridge Wells, where the sandwiches were slightly stale and the only thing on the radio was 'Sing Something Simple'.

I vowed by his bed that day that I would try my very best to continue his work of making poetry real. To make it startle. To make it count. I'll never forget what he said to me once – drunk, of course, the familiar roll-up cigarette burning down to nothing in his hand. 'Hamilton,' he said, 'you're the kind of poet that makes people want to listen to other poets.'

I'm seriously considering having that written on my gravestone.

21

MOURNING TIDE

It took Paul and Sophie quite a while to come to terms with Wiverly's death.

PAUL: I grieved. Sophie grieved. We both grieved. Sometimes we grieved together. Sometimes we grieved alone. I often grieved with complete strangers. There was something oddly cathartic in that – just sitting on a park bench, say, and when someone sat down, letting it all out. Or in the supermarket. People were mostly very kind. I think people in the Far East have got their grieving right. They shout, they cry, they hit their heads. We just button it all up. If you're reading this and you're grieving at the moment, for God's sake don't sit on it. Let it out. In the cinema, on the bus. You'll feel better for it. And I think you'll be surprised at the amount of sympathy you receive.

We took ourselves off to the Algarve. Sophie's sister has a villa there. We were both just so stunned. We were pole-axed by our sadness, really. All we could do during the day was lie in the sun. Maybe swim a little. There's something about swimming that helps with grief. It did for me, at any rate. Maybe it's because I'm not very good at it. As I concentrated on the strokes I'd almost forget about the pain for a while. But once I was back by the poolside it would all come flooding back. Reading helped a little, and I have to say a few drinks did dull the ache. Surprisingly, we both had quite an appetite during that period. I think it was probably all the swimming.

We grieved for about six months. Dark days. Darker nights. Gradually though, almost imperceptibly, my grief started to lessen in its intensity. One day, I suddenly found myself involuntarily laughing out loud at something in one of Nigel Rees's books on graffiti. I forget what it was now. I was astonished. Although my laughter faded after a few seconds, I continued to not feel indescribably sad for nearly five minutes. This was a breakthrough. Over the next fortnight or so the gaps between feeling utterly bereft became longer and longer. There was a minor set-back when I was mugged by three street kids in a market, but I was only slightly winded and luckily I was on my way to the bank, so it didn't make too much of a dent in my pocket or, more importantly, in my general sense of progress. Then, one evening over a prawn dish, I said to Sophie, 'You know, I think it's time for us to stop grieving and move on.' Sophie suggested Tunisia, but I told her I felt we should start thinking about returning to England. To reality.

To my wonderment, during the tail end of my time in Portugal I began to feel the stirrings of new poems. Original poems. Paul Hamilton poems. Just a verse here, a line there. It was incredible. Up until then I had only ever come up with just six poems that I was reasonably happy with. However, one of them was so exceptionally emotionally raw that I had found myself physically unable to write it down, let alone read it out. A second poem was so sexually explicit, recalling an erotic experience Sophie and I had had on a roundabout after a drunken spree, that I had felt obliged, for modesty's sake, to destroy it. And so at this point I actually had only four poems that were of any practical use. But now new energy was starting to flow. I could feel it coming: the spring thaw after the winter freeze. On top of that I had a dream one night, and it seemed to be some kind of message. In the dream I was standing on what can only be described as a raised platform and I was speaking into a tube with wire coming from it. Two words were written on the wall behind me: 'verse' and 'society'. There were other people there, and some of them were also taking the tube and speaking into it. They were a fantastical bunch of characters: I recognised Dylan Thomas, Ted Hughes and Seamus Heaney, although Seamus Heaney was also Su Pollard. It made absolutely no sense to me, but when I related it to Sophie she immediately said, 'Oh my god, don't you see? The dream is telling you you should open a poetry club!'

Of course, once she said that and I thought about it, it seemed blindingly obvious. I think it must have been the Su Pollard element that confused me. But there you go, that's Sophie – she can see right past the surface stuff in a way that often makes me feel ashamed. That was exactly what my creative id was urging me to do: open a poetry club. We booked our tickets and were back in London in less than six weeks.

22

POST-POST-MORTEM

SOPHIE: When we got back, I thought it was time Paul and I made a bit of a commitment, so I dropped some pretty heavy hints about moving into a place together, just the two of us. He didn't pick up on a single one, of course, scatterbrain that he is, so in the end I just came right out with it. He said, 'Well, we already live together.' And I said, 'Yes, but not just the two of us. There's Suzy too' – she was the other tenant. And he said, 'Yes, but we hardly see her. If she's not at work, she's in her room most of the time.' And I said, 'Yes, but a couple who are committed to each other need freedom and privacy. What if', I said, 'we want to walk around naked and drunk? We can't very well do that if Suzy is about.' And he said, 'But you already walk around naked and drunk – and, come to that, so does Suzy when she's had a few.' And I said, 'Yes, but that's not the point.' And it went on and on like this until it all got a bit heated and I ended up shouting at him and telling him he was a selfish bastard and he obviously didn't care and that I was moving out to live on my own.

Well. Bless. By the end of the week he'd taken me out for a Thai and between courses presented me with a set of keys. I said, 'What are these for?' And he said, 'For our flat. I've rented somewhere just for us!'

I was so excited! He took me to see it, blindfolding me before he led me in. When he took the blindfold

off, I couldn't believe my eyes. It was an absolute hovel.
No furniture, holes in the wall and it stank. And it was
in Streatham. I mean, Streatham! Please! But it was the
thought that counted. So I gave him a great big hug, told
him to leave it to me, tapped Daddy for a little help and
we ended up renting a very nice little loft conversion in
Primrose Hill.

PAUL: As soon as we were back from Portugal – I can't
remember whose idea it was, possibly mine – we decided
that we should find a place of our own. It seemed very
clear to us that we would be sticking together. That done,
we started looking for a suitable venue for the poetry club.
We looked at a lot of places. We looked in Highgate, Highbury, even Kentish Town. But there was always something
not quite right: too off the beaten track, philistine land-
lords, sport on the television – you name it. But we found
it in the end. As soon as I walked through the doors of the
Cocked Hat, five minutes from the Angel tube in Islington, I knew that this was it.

Owned by Thomas and Morag O'Neill, third-generation
North London Irish, the Cocked Hat sat, small and rather
gloomy, in a small London side street, as it had done since
before the First World War. It was quiet, a little dowdy and
had a little back room used principally to store Thomas
O'Neill's old Norton motorbike.

SOPHIE: Oh, I adored it from the off. It was so quaint. We
got chatting to Thomas and told him what we were after. He wasn't keen at first, said he didn't want to disturb

his regulars. By 'regulars' he meant four little old gnomey chaps who all sat with their Guinnesses night after night, staring at an old black-and-white TV in the corner. They were so sweet! Thomas mentioned the back room, and I asked if we could see it. I have to say, I think it was the fact that he was rather a fan of the larger lady which more or less sealed the deal. I know that look they get in their eye, you see. All I had to do was slip into flirty mode, flutter my eyelashes a bit, hoist up the cleavage and *voilà*, poor old soul never stood a chance. He said he'd have to talk it over with his wife, so I gave him my number and off we popped. Funniest thing about that evening was that Paul got all jealous. When we got outside, he started on one of his rants: 'Couldn't you make it a little bit more obvious that you fancied that ludicrous old leprechaun!' That kind of thing. Actually, when he gets all possessive like that it gets me a bit horny. Sorry! Too much information! Anyway, I just let him warble on. It's always best; you know he'll tire himself out eventually. When he'd finished, I pointed out to him that tiny old duffers with purple noses aren't really my thing, and that I'd been playing the saucy mare to win the good landlord over. That calmed him down.

The next day Tom called Sophie and told her his wife had agreed and they could hire the back room for £30 per night or 10 per cent of the takings, whichever was the higher amount.

PAUL: It was an added bonus that it was, essentially, an Irish pub. I've such a huge respect for the Irish and the way they've come through a hell of a time over the centuries. My grandfather was Irish. He had to come over to England in the twenties for work. He couldn't get any in Ireland. There was a lot of prejudice at the time against Irish men who had been in the Black and Tans.

Sophie and Paul set to publicising their new venue. The first thing, though, was to think up a name for it. It was Sophie with her love of hip hop who came up with the final choice.

SOPHIE: 'Word Up' is one of my favourite tracks ever. You know, Cameo, about 1987 or something? And I thought, 'Well, you know, poetry has words, and the song has also got "up" in it, which is quite a positive word, isn't it?'

PAUL: I must admit we'd been floundering for a week trying to find a name for the venue. 'Poetry Pub', 'Poems Out the Back', 'Poetry and Pint Pots' – that was a favourite for a while. When Sophie played me 'Word Up', it just seemed perfect. As soon as I heard it I had absolutely no choice other than to get up and then proceed in no uncertain terms to get down. I knew instinctively it would be pretty damn cool to blast it out on Sophie's ghetto blaster immediately before the first poet took to the stage, just to show that we weren't the usual bunch of Leonard Cohen-listening jumper wearers. I thought it would be a great idea to get a local kid to do a paint-spray graffiti of 'Word Up' on the back wall of the room but, sadly, I didn't have any luck finding anyone to do it. I approached a couple of graffitists but, it pains me to say, they were pretty uncommunicative. They didn't really trust a stranger in their 'hood, it seems, so I didn't ever get a chance to explain what I wanted, which is a real shame. That's the way it is, though. When you're in your teens and you're a little bit out on the edge of things, everyone over twenty-five looks like The Man. That's certainly my memory of how it was at that age, so it's understandable.

Paul and Sophie started an upbeat publicity campaign to bring in audiences for the twice-monthly poetry-reading nights at 'Word Up'.

PAUL: Think of this if you can: no Internet. That's right. Well, there was, but it was pretty rudimentary. And personally, at the time I wouldn't have known a modem from some Imodium. And so when it came to advertising 'Word Up', we did it old style. We took out ads in *Time Out* and *City Limits*. We paid for a bundle of posters and fly-posted all over the Camden, Highbury and Archway districts. Most daringly, we went into other poetry clubs and surreptitiously handed out flyers. This was somewhat risky because most people running poetry clubs were very possessive of their audiences. If you got caught, there could be trouble. It got quite unpleasant one evening, when the owner of a club quite near the Cocked Hat came up to me as I was handing a flyer to one of her punters at the bar and asked for a private word. She led me to a quiet space in the beer garden and asked me if I thought that perhaps it was a little 'uncool' to be advertising a competing club in another club. I countered that what was 'uncool' was the attempted monopolisation of what was, after all, a free art form. I knew damn well she couldn't say a thing to that. It was a shame, because after that showdown our previously friendly chats after chance meetings in the aisles of our local Waitrose supermarket were never less than tense and stilted.

Sophie and I were pretty thorough. As the opening night loomed, I felt convinced that we were on the threshold of something truly remarkable.

23

A FALSE START

On 3 August 1992 'Word Up' presented its first night of poetry. It wasn't a rip-roaring success.

PAUL: I'd booked five poets, with myself as the compère. I was pretty nervous. For a start I'd never MC'd before. When I'd been in bands with Charlie, it was always he who did the talking between numbers. I had only seven poems that I was prepared to perform publicly, and I had not yet mastered the art of just chatting generally to an audience. I knew I was going to have to keep the compèring side of things pretty brief. But I needn't have worried too much. By half past eight the only people in the room were me, Sophie, four of the poets I'd booked (the fifth had pulled out due to his gout flaring up), the landlord Tom and the four regulars. The latter, incidentally, had all breezed non-chalantly right past Sophie, who was on the door, poised to take the £5 entrance fee.

Rather than cancel, we all gamely agreed that 'the show must go on', and finally, at twelve minutes past nine, I took to the small performing area as the grinding groove of our theme song 'Word Up' faded down and stammering-ly uttered my 'Good evening.' The first poet was a young Mancunian guy who I thought held a lot of promise, even though he was shaking so much with nerves that the rus-tling of the pieces of paper he was holding drowned out a lot of what he was saying. Halfway through his slot the old regulars started up an unselfconscious conversation between themselves. When Sophie shushed them, they looked at her for a couple of moments in total bafflement before simply continuing where they'd left off. Just after the second poet started – a self-proclaimed white witch whose name was something Gaelic – the old fellows stood up and, still chatting and laughing, noisily ambled out and back into the bar. They never came in again. When the witch had finished, I asked the other two poets if they wanted to carry on and, bless them, they did. The dispiriting opening night of 'Word Up' ended with a lock-in in the bar, Sophie and I sitting with the regulars, drowning our sorrows. I'm afraid I got rather maudlin. Just before he shambled to the door one of the regulars, Sean, put a calloused hand on my shoulder and said, 'What you need to bring the punters in, my son, is a couple of strippers.' Everyone laughed at that.

Except me.

We redoubled our efforts at publicising the club. We put more posters up, took out bigger ads, extended them to book shops, libraries and health-food emporia. The second night no one came. The third night no one came. The fourth night three men in business suits came in. They were from Leicester and had come to London for a double-glazing sales convention. They had been wandering from pub to pub since five o'clock and were now so drunk they didn't really know where they were, and anyway were all asleep five minutes after sitting down.

I was at my wit's end. Here I was at the age of thirty-three, a poet with just seven poems to his canon whose poetry club was on its way to closing down before it had even got going. In short, I was a complete and utter failure.

That night Sophie and I had the most violent argument we have ever had, before or since. It was all my fault. As we were stacking the un-sat-upon chairs I selfishly started picking on her, blaming her design of the flyers for being the reason people were staying away. I had always thought lime green a rather garish colour, whereas Sophie maintained that it was eye-catching. The point was immaterial, really. I was just lashing out. Did I mention that Sophie is a very passionate woman? Well, she lashed out back and nearly knocked me unconscious in the process. As she picked me up and brushed me down she told me she was going to take herself off to consider whether she ever wanted to see me again.

I told her I didn't care whether I ever saw her again. And at the time I meant it. What followed turned out to be what I later came to call my 'lost week'.

24

LIMBO NUMBER 2

SOPHIE: So, yes, that crack about my flyers was the last straw. He'd been an unbearable little ratbag for weeks up until then because 'Word Up' had been so slow, and when he started blaming me I just thought, 'Oh gosh, you know what, you ridiculous little cock?' and, pow, down he went. I'm awful when I get my dander up. Red mist! Anyway, next day I thought, 'Right! I'm off to have a bloody good time!' And that's exactly what I did. Called up a few old boyfriends and, well, naughty Sophie! I must say, though, personally speaking, it really did clear the cobwebs away.

PAUL: At the time I had been working for a few weeks at an upmarket eatery called Victoria's Delicatessen. It belonged to a snooty guy called Peregrine and was basically a sandwich bar for toffs, with a sideline in deliveries. 'Quality catering for the professionals' was what the copperplate writing on the shop sign boasted. 'Overpriced finger food for posh nobs' was my take on it. I found myself joining an ever-changing staff of some nine or ten out-of-work actors and struggling artists. All sorts, really. A good bunch. They may have been buttering baguettes but they hadn't given up on their dreams. And some of them eventually realised those dreams. (By the way, hi to Gregg Haynes. It was great to see you as the rapist in *Midsomer Murders* a few years back. I had a feeling you'd do OK.)

There were life's victims as well. I'll never forget Sylvia. Sweet, shy Sylvia. Her confidence had been destroyed after being sacked as a waitress at the Savoy after fifteen years of faithful service solely because her glass eye fell into Joan Collins's soup. Hey, the Savoy, it was an accident. Accidents happen. But still, here was Sylvia, reduced to washing salad for a fat Tory for £2 an hour. Well done, the Savoy. You must be so proud.

Every day telephoned orders from some moneyed firm of solicitors or PR company would be obsequiously taken by Peregrine and then passed on to the harassed kitchen staff. Having been fastidiously prepared and arranged on silver-foil serving platters, these were then handed to me to attach to the rear-wheel rack of an old, unwieldy bicycle and off I would totter.

At work the morning after the big fall-out with Sophie I loaded two tray-loads of food onto the delivery bike. However, when I arrived at the headquarters of the financial-services company I was supposed to be delivering to, I just kept pedalling. I now realise I must have been in a deep depression. I had no idea where I was heading; I just kept looking straight ahead and pushing on those pedals. I was in a daze.

Hours passed. I did not stop. Finally, I found myself coming out of my trance. I was still pedalling but the streets of London had long slipped away, as had the colourless, serried rows of outlying suburbia. I found myself flanked by green fields. I was on a small B road far from home. Unaware, lost in misery, I had unwittingly cycled into unchartered territory. Here I was, alone, the light fading, somewhere, God knew where, in the depths of Surrey.

Strangely, I did not panic. I suppose because I was so depressed I simply did not care. It was too far and I was too tired to cycle back the way I had come. I would have to find shelter for the night. Luckily it was a fairly mild September night. I have since surmised that if I had taken leave of my senses on a freezing February morning, I would have perished in the fields and been fed upon by the shivering crow, the quaking vole and the trembling worm, would have warmed them, nourished them with my cold flesh before being returned through them to take my place among the clods and sods. A not unfitting demise for a poet, I feel. But my time had not yet come. Across a field in the golden twilight I could see a barn. With some difficulty I lifted the bike over the barbed-wire fence and wheeled it over. I reached the barn in no time and, with some bales of hay as my mattress and my pacamac as my duvet, I lay down and fell into one of the deepest sleeps I have ever experienced.

Over the next five days I gradually became stripped of my modern-day identity. Something in me, it seems, wanted to return to the very basics, to an utterly primitive level of living. I was escaping the issues in my life that I could not face. Deep down I was terrified that I had lost not only Sophie but just about everything else besides and, in retrospect, I realise that I was acting on a strong subconscious urge to go back to the beginning and start all over again.

Those who have ever been called upon to fend for themselves in the wild will know just how difficult that is for we pampered moisturiser-men. We have lost the ancient arts, the skills our distant forefathers knew, which were taught to them by their fathers in a lineage stretching back many thousands of years. Much as I honour him and am grateful for the gift of life, all my father ever taught me was the battles of the Crimean war, in order of the number of casualties, and how to put up a deckchair.

And, now, here I was, far from the city and with just my wits to help keep me alive. Could I trap and kill a rabbit? Skin it, start a fire from scratch and then cook that rabbit? Obviously I could not, and so I was grateful indeed for the coronation-chicken sandwiches, Spanish tortilla and sausage rolls on the back of the delivery bike. Even so, by the end of the second day, and despite the protection of their silver-foil covering, the sandwiches were beginning to become stale, the tortilla claggy, the sausage rolls soggy. Strangely, I found myself unconcerned. I started feeling elemental, at one with the land. As the hours passed I began behaving more and more on the level of pure instinct. At night I howled at the moon (though not too loudly, for I feared discovery), and then slept a dark and dreamless sleep. By day I became a stalking, silent thing, ranging the fields, ducking and avoiding the dog walkers and ramblers. It was one of the strangest and yet most liberating experiences of my life. When you have spent time quietly standing naked with a herd of cows or bathing in a pig's water trough, what seems so important in so-called normal everyday life fades into total insignificance.

Meanwhile, Sophie was living it up.

SOPHIE: One of the old flames I hooked up with asked me to marry him. I seem to remember we were halfway through our fourth bottle of rum. I thought it was a terrific idea. Apparently I even suggested it would be really super to have a beach wedding in Java conducted by a Kebatinan holy man. I mean, I ask you! Didn't come to my senses till we were in the taxi halfway to Heathrow. Narrow escape. But then I've had plenty of those!

After five days Paul's self-imposed exile from civilisation was coming to an end.

PAUL: I continued my aboriginal episode, surrendering myself to the elements, to the earth and sky. Somewhere deep inside me, though, I knew that this was temporary. And when I took hold of the very last of the Scotch eggs, I knew that it would soon be time to go back to my old life. And yet I knew, too, that it would not be the old life but a new one.

Sure enough, I awoke on the morning of my sixth day in the wilderness knowing for certain that I was not where I belonged. That it was time, right now, to leave. On opening my eyes I was greeted by the sight of the farmer who owned the barn. He seemed irate and was prodding me with a shotgun. I felt no animosity over my rude awakening. I'm sure we're all aware of what a fantastic job the farmers of Great Britain do, but they are simple creatures and, as he saw it, I was encroaching on his territory and must be seen off. I could offer no resistance to this good soul, and so I quickly gathered myself together and – with a few choice words from that doughty son of the soil to speed me on my way – I wheeled the bike back across the field to the road. I was cold, I was aching, but, in that grey dawn light, I felt strangely reborn.

Later that morning, sitting in the cabin of a lorry driven by a racist from Antwerp, I knew that things were going to be different.

The first thing I had to do on my return was woo Sophie back. She had no idea what I had been through, no inkling that I had realised I would never undervalue her again. I wrote her a long letter, explaining my love for her and apologising for all the occasions I had mistreated her: the time I had spooned mayonnaise all over a painting-by-numbers she was painstakingly working on just because she had accidentally lost my favourite pen; the time I had criticised the moussaka she had baked for my birthday; the time I had betrayed her with an acupuncturist. I was guilty of any number of small and not so small unkindnesses, and I knew I must make amends. There wasn't an immediate answer. That was a pretty hairy few days, I can tell you. But eventually she called. She came back to me. She told me she'd been taking time out too. I think we'd both just needed time apart. For some serious reappraisal. Always painful to a certain extent but, by God, sometimes it's just what needs to be done.

SOPHIE: Yes, well, after a week of being a very bad Sophie indeed I ended up back at Mummy and Daddy's, and there was this really sweet letter waiting for me. I thought, 'Oh, what's the use, there's no fighting it.' That man. I mean, I must be potty or something. All my friends think so. But I can't fight it. He just does something to me.

25

COGGS

After his week-long disappearance Paul returned to the sandwich shop to hand in his notice, only to find that not only had he been sacked, but the theft of the delivery bike had been reported to the police. He was let off with a caution.

'Word Up' continued to limp along. One night they had twenty people in, a party of Japanese tourists who, due to a booking error, had been unable to secure tickets for the musical *Wicked*. After quickly scanning the listings, their desperate holiday guide had resorted to 'Word Up' as a last-minute replacement for an experience of genuine English culture. The party sat in polite but largely uncomprehending silence as five poets verbally bared their all in far from plain English.

Paul's fortunes were to take a turn when veteran American poet Lenny Coggs walked into his life.

PAUL: It was another pretty quiet night, as usual. Maybe ten people in. And then during the interval in walked this old guy with long pink hair who was wearing some sort of cloak. He was surrounded by six or seven people, some his age, some younger, who seemed to be hanging on his every word. I had absolutely no idea who he was, but then Stephanie Chambers, our headlining poet, came up to me, virtually hyperventilating. She was whispering in my ear,

'Look who it is, look who it is!' I said, 'Who?' She said, 'There, him, the guy with the cloak. That's Lenny Coggs.' I have to admit, I'd never heard of him.

Born in Fresno in 1930, Lenny Coggs moved to San Francisco in the early fifties and fell in with the underground scene that was blossoming at the time. Hanging out with hip poets such as Kenneth Rexroth and Robert Duncan, he had minor publishing successes with books of poetry such as *Kipper Fat* and *Money Down Your Barrel*. He never really achieved big-time celebrity but, to a small group of diehard fans, he was, and is still, very highly regarded. This is the man who pulled his trousers down in front of Allen Ginsberg and then handed him a knife, daring him to cut off his penis and eat it. Ginsberg famously replied, 'Thanks, man, I already ate.' This is the man who took peyote mushrooms with Jim Morrison in 1967 and nearly tipped the singer into permanent psychosis by spending the entire trip pretending to be a giant worm.

Whether sucking on a toothpick-thin joint at the back of a shot in a Russ Meyer movie, or being charged with assault after attempting to dance the flamenco with Ronald Reagan during a campaign walkabout, Coggs continued making his own unique contribution to the counter-culture through the decades until his death in 2009.

In 1994 Coggs came to Britain to study Druidism and to 'sparkle in olde London town for a while'. After spotting a poster advertising the 'Word Up' club in the window of a head shop, he decided he would drop in and check it out. It was a decision that would change everything for Paul.

On arriving at the venue, Coggs was introduced to Paul by one of his companions, and then proceeded to sit with his group and smoke powerful joints, causing a panicked Paul to rush to a nearby corner shop to buy air freshener, which he sprayed as discreetly as possible so that the strong smell of the weed wouldn't attract any unwanted attention from the front bar. Coggs brought with him an open and festive atmosphere and soon, it seems, the carefully planned schedule of the evening counted for nothing. Paul was keen to get the second half of the show going, but all of the poets on the bill that night and the few poetry fans who comprised the actual audience were now crowded around Coggs and his friends, exchanging laughter and friendly banter. Not to mention joints. Thrilled to have such an entertaining luminary among them, it was impossible to pull them away. The poetry element of the evening only got going again when Coggs was finally persuaded to get up and give an impromptu performance. He improvised for nearly an hour and a half. After time had been called, Tom, the landlord, was quite happy to lock the door, and by one o'clock in the morning the audience, the poets and Coggs and his friends were in an extremely happy state of intoxication. When it was finally time to leave, numbers were exchanged, with Coggs claiming, as he downed his umpteenth Jack Daniels, that this gig was 'hopping'. His parting shot as he was carried out of the door was, 'I'll be here next time − if there is such a thing!'

He was as good as his word. And just as well, for the other poets and the small audience at 'Word Up' that night had spread the word and, come eight o'clock on the next date, the small room was heaving with over fifty people.

'Word Up' was indeed up. And running. The knock-on effect was that poets with their own followings started calling Paul and asking him for gigs. Anything to share a bill with Lenny Coggs.

By early 1993 'Word Up' was enjoying a steady audience of thirty or so paying punters – even after Coggs had returned to San Francisco. Paul was earning enough to get by. Just.

PAUL: Oh, it was tight. But I didn't care. Remember, I'd come pretty close to starvation at one point. The faintest light was visible on the horizon. I started to let myself dare believe that perhaps the long night was beginning to be over.

26

TEDIUM

In 1994, as things were slowly starting to gain momentum for Paul, I started working, along with several other performers, on a project called Cluub Zarathustra, a politico-art 'statement' overseen by a rather otherworldly individual called The League Against Tedium.

What can I say about 'The League', as we used to call him affectionately? Not much, actually. He was a complete enigma, and remains so. There were rumours that he'd been recruited by MI5 as a code breaker in the early eighties, when barely in his teens. When I quizzed him on this, he told me that the only code he had ever broken was the one for DNA, and that that was a personal matter he was not prepared to discuss.

We were all fairly certain that he was a genius. He was convinced. He definitely had all the external hallmarks: glasses, one pair of trousers, no fixed hairstyle. We were constantly astonished by his obsessive application to any project, concept or phenomenon that drew his attention, be it electric gloves, the rewriting of the alphabet or the consumption of lager. For example, in the late nineties he decided to invent an alter ego for himself. He felt that one simply wasn't enough. And so the character of 'Simon Munnery' , stand-up comedian and family man, was born. The League still regularly immerses himself in this identity and can often be seen appearing as 'Simon Munnery' at comedy venues around the country. Typical of his total engagement in any venture that he involves himself with he has even gone so far as to marry, father three children and buy a property in the Bedford area, all while 'in character'.

It was around this time that I bumped into Paul and his partner Sophie at a family get-together. I had seen my cousin only one or twice since we were teenagers. He and Sophie seemed to me to be an unlikely couple on the surface of it, but it was clear there was a lot of affection between them. Paul seemed generally fired up about life. He talked enthusiastically and at length about his poetry. It was good to hear that he had found his 'vocation', as he referred to it. When I mentioned Cluub Zarathustra in passing, Sophie said that it sounded very interesting and promised that the two of them would come along and check it out. Sure enough, come the next show there they were in the front row.

After the show had finished Paul seemed very impressed.

PAUL: Cluub Zarathustra was shambolic, under-rehearsed, wilfully obtuse, self-indulgent, amateurish and often in questionable taste. The performers seemed drunk and showed little or no consideration for their paying audience. I loved it. The first time I saw it I thought, 'What the hell are these guys doing?' And then halfway through I realised. They had given themselves the right to fail and, having done that, had the guts to exercise that right again and again. The whole show blew me away. But it was the guy in charge who rocked my horse. The League Against Tedium. I don't know what the hell that man put in his soup, but it should be available on the National Health Service (while there still is one).

I knew I had to try my utmost be a part of this anarchy, so I approached Kevin afterwards and asked if there'd be any chance of me doing some of my poetry. He said he would ask the League Against Tedium and get back to me. I endured a feverish two-week wait before I got a response. I had been accepted. Or, as the actual message from the League put it, my 'usage' had been 'sanctioned', with the caveat 'but when you weep, and weep you shall, do so far away. And preferably under water.'

It felt terrific to be welcomed on board. And what a trip. What a ride. I wasn't in that madhouse for long, but I treasure every second of my time there. It was certainly a privilege to work with the League. Even though he rarely talked to me or even really looked at me, I sensed an unspoken empathy. I guess it was just the natural mutual respect you get between two people trying to strike out from the beaten path.

I wanted to interview the League about his memories of Paul. When I contacted 'Simon Munnery' about this, he told me he would ask him, but I was not to hold out much hope as the League was very busy. Sensing the hall of mirrors that this implied I thought that this line of enquiry might well not yield anything. I had just given up hope of getting any feedback when, to my delight, I received a letter from the League written in red ink (blood?) on what appeared to be toilet paper, detailing some reminiscences of Paul's time with Cluub Zarathustra.

THE LEAGUE AGAINST TEDIUM: Hamilton? Ah. He was always there, like a stain. I loved him, yes, not as a brother, more as a goat. Yes, I remember Hamilton. Well, not remember exactly – that would be overstating the matter. Poets were despised back then, poetry being seen as an unprofitable branch of mental illness. All the more reason to allow him in. The only literature I valued was the Haynes manuals, *Reader's Digest* and the indentations left in the cheek by a jackboot. His finest moment was his '24-Hour Poetry Marathon Inside a Locked Soundproof Box'. I persuaded him to do it with the help of one of the Cluub Zarathustra sub-wormes. Or 'an actress', as I believe it liked to call itself. It was great, truly great; the relief was palpable. And I think in the end it was nearer to forty-eight hours. It was amazing the effect his poems had on an audience: they made anything, absolutely anything that came afterwards seem entertaining. That is what made his slot essential in the show.

Paul was to perform sporadically with them for over a year. When his 'usage' was no longer 'sanctioned' and his term with Cluub Zarathustra came to an end, he was notified in a manner wholly characteristic of the League: he received a publicity shot of the Cluub Zarathustra ensemble, with a black cross in felt-tip pen over his face. There was no stamp and Paul was obliged to pay the postage.

PAUL: Listen. No hard feelings. That was just the League for you. I hardly expected a P45 and a carriage clock. And quite frankly, being part of that for any great length of time . . . there are only so many performances you can take where the audience walk out or demand their money back or get on stage and assault you before it starts getting a little dispiriting. Christ, though, talk about character building.

Paul was unfazed by his dismissal. His confidence in performing his poetry live had grown, and as a result he had started getting more and more spots at various poetry nights around London. It wasn't long before he was securing bookings further afield.

PAUL: Yeah. I guess '94 was the year I kind of took flight. I started getting invited to all sorts of spoken-word events all over the country. That's the fantastic part about being a performing poet: you get to experience so many facets of society directly. I've been booked to read my poetry in such a wide range of venues: community centres, arts centres, leisure centres . . . you name it. But it's the sheer range of people I meet that offers the greatest reward: from the woman who had the largest collection of paintings of parrots in the world to a man who, at a garden party at Buckingham Palace in 1974, had bowed so suddenly that he'd accidentally headbutted the Queen Mother.

I count myself blessed.

27

INCEPTIONS, REJECTIONS AND REDEMPTIONS

By mid-1995 Paul had written just fifteen poems. I asked him about his comparatively slow rate of output.

PAUL: This has been my personal hell all along the way: the sheer difficulty of writing decent bloody poetry. I'm not exaggerating. It is agony. I don't like to talk about it because it's a very personal thing. When it comes to quality control I am very hard on myself. But I wouldn't have it any other way. I reject so very much more than I accept. Do you remember those John West adverts? It's like that. I find the whole process of bringing a poem into the world as painful as giving birth. I know I'm not a woman and that some mothers would take exception and ask how would I know about their pain, but I would suggest that those mothers are not poets, so how would they know about mine? So, really, and I don't mean this disrespectfully, they should shut up.

It's different for every poem of course, but usually the vague beginnings of an idea slowly start forming in the womb of my mind, if I may carry on with the natal analogy. I think the longest 'gestation period' for a poem of mine was for one called 'Bent Spoonerism'. How did it begin . . . 'Guri Yeller, funny feller . . .' Yeah. I don't do it any more, but it's very me circa '92/'93. That took fifteen months to develop, which, I think, is about the time it takes from inception for a giraffe to be born. The shortest took just under three minutes. I believe some types of microbes can merge and reproduce in about that time. Ironically, that would have been one of my longer works: a twelve-stanza piece on the death of Labour leader John Smith. Tragically, I wrote it so quickly, in such a fit of passion, that when I came to read it back it was totally illegible. And that was it. Gone from my mind. I couldn't read a word of it and I couldn't remember a word of it. I do know it was bloody good, though. This is painful to me but, you know, looking back, quite a few poems never made it. And that's still the case. But I guess that's because they just weren't strong enough. Also, there are a few that, regrettably, I've had to put down. There was one about Tamagotchis. And another about Piers Morgan. They were of their time, but they just lost their relevance. I miss the ones that have fallen by the wayside; I'd be some kind of heartless bastard if I didn't. Darwin's theory of the survival of the fittest definitely extends to poems, as far as I'm concerned. I guess you could call it the Theory of P-volution. I don't know. I'm just floating that. But, anyway, let's not get mawkish. The ones that have made it . . . I'm as proud as any parent of his children. And I've watched them grow and mature. But there are more to come, I hope. The good thing about poems is that, unlike children, they don't draw on the furniture and they don't bite you on the calf for absolutely no good reason.

In October 1995 Paul gathered his fifteen poems together in one document, wrote a short introduction and set
about trying to get them published as an anthology entitled *Shadows of Reflections*. It was to prove a frustratingly
difficult task.

PAUL: Well, you can see how particular I am about the
standard of my poetry. I only had fifteen but as far as I was
concerned they were all top notch. So I started sending
them off as a batch, as *Shadows of Reflections*. And it was
always the same. It didn't matter how many follow-up letters you dispatched or phone calls you made, six months
later back would come what you'd sent, with the standard
rejection slip: 'Thank you for your interest in blah blah.
We feel your work does not fit the current profile of our
blah blah but we do wish you all the blah blah blah.'

I don't take rejection very well. I suppose I ought to be
upfront about that. What the hell? I'm a passionate guy.

SOPHIE: Oh, his rejection letters? I used to dread them.
Once he screamed at a rejection slip for what must have
been a whole minute. He really hurt his voice terribly. Had
to go to the docs. Turned out he'd actually ruptured his
larynx. He'd get awfully blue. I remember after opening
one, from Virago I think it was, he locked himself in the
bathroom for five hours. I could hear these awful gargling
noises in there. Took me a while to work out that he was
sitting in the shower moaning with his head pointing up
towards the stream of water. There was another occasion
when he seemed to be reacting to a rejection letter in a
really positive way, you know, disappointed but philo-

sophical, and I thought, 'Oh, goody, he's finally learning how to handle them,' but when I went into the kitchen he was sitting at the table rubbing spag bol into his hair. The worst was when he got one from Penguin. He set fire to it, then burned his fingers and dropped it onto a papier mâché head of Bob Marley I'd been working on for the Notting Hill carnival. Well, that went up, whoosh, just like that. Next thing we knew the curtains were in flames and we had to call the fire brigade. Hideously embarrassing. I'd spent three weeks making that head, too. I couldn't believe it, but he actually told the fire guys how the blaze started. They were so cross. Just before they left the last fireman got Paul up against the wall and told him next time he got a rejection slip, rather than set fire to it, he should bring it to the fire station because they'd know what to do with it. Paul thought that was all terribly unprofessional, but I honestly couldn't blame the fire guy for getting in a strop, not least because he was absolutely scrummy. He could have put me up against a wall any time. Anyway, after that I banned Paul from opening letters from publishers in the house. He had to go to the park down the road.

PAUL: That's the thing with rejection, though. You start thinking to yourself, 'What if the people rejecting me really do know what they're talking about and actually aren't talentless, narrow-minded, complacent mediocrities content to eke out their shallow, cowardly existences passing unqualified judgement on people they are not fit to wipe the bottoms of?' And that's exactly the kind of ludicrous thought process that constant rejection can actually reduce you to in moments of weakness. But you have to stay strong. You have to be prepared to stay the course. Alan Rickman, one of my favourite actors – I love the truth of the guy – didn't get his first movie role until he was forty-six. Peter Roget didn't see his thesaurus published until he was seventy-three. Seventy-three, for God's sake. What if he'd lost the faith in his mid-sixties and just given up? Jacked it in? Thrown in the towel? Alexander Fleming, he was no spring chicken when he invented penicillin. He may have taken his time, but I think we all agree it was worth it, as anybody who has been a martyr to non-specific urethritis all his life will be happy to tell you.

Guys like those were my inspiration. They kept the flame of hope burning for me. I got knocked back and knocked back. But now look, I'm fifty-five and finally I'm published.

I'm published.

Me.

Published.

28

SCREEN TIME

In the spring of 1999 Paul was contacted by Channel 4 producer Robert Katz, who was looking to make a fifteen-minute programme for the late-night culture slot *Night Art*.

PAUL: That was a little out of the blue. I didn't really know how to react to Robert's offer. I have always been suspicious of television, or rather the abuse thereof by those in charge of it. These days that suspicion has curdled into a mouldering hatred. I see modern-day television as a stinking carcass swinging in the ether, its rotting meat all that is left of the once great promise of mass communication. Mass communication? Miscommunication is what it has become. What has it to offer? Art? You'll find precious little art worthy of consideration but, hey, how about an evening watching some silicone-piped popsy necking maggots for money. Shakespeare? Who he? Let us savour rather the cut-and-paste clichés of production-line am dram, in which meat-faced synthetic cockneys bellow at each other without resorting to a single consonant. And poetry? Noetry. Surely we'd much rather ingest the spectacle of some auto-tuned illiterate wheedling his protestations of idiot lust to a pack of squawking delta-proles.

And that's the pick of the week, folks.

Admittedly, back in '99 things hadn't quite come to the pass that they have in the last ten years or so, but nevertheless, even then, to switch on the television was the equivalent of condemning one's senses to unextraordinary rendition.

SOPHIE: Oh gosh, Paul was so thrilled! We both were. I remember him coming off the phone and grabbing hold of me and jumping up and down. 'I'm going to be on television! Me! On television!' I thought he'd finally made it onto *Countdown*. He used to send in three or four applications a year. Had a big thing going for Carol Vorderman. But it was better than that: somebody at Channel 4 wanted to make a programme just about him. I thought, 'Gosh, who'd've believed it!' I mean, most people didn't know him from Adam, and now, apparently, he was going to be on his own programme, broadcasting to the whole country. We were both thrilled.

PAUL: I thought, 'OK, well let's see what exactly is on the table here.' I knew I that if I agreed to do something, it was vital I maintained strict control over how my poems were presented. I immediately set to writing down ideas to offer to the producer and director. I have recently dug out the notes and re-read them. They're maybe a little adventurous, a couple of them, but they show the kind of vision I had.

1. Book Albert Hall and film me reading there to a packed audience.
2. Film me by starting on a close-up and pulling back a little further at the start of each poem to finally reveal after the last poem that I am standing alone on an ice floe in the Arctic Ocean.

3. Alternate me reading with quality actors reading on stage at the Globe theatre. Suggestions: Alan Rickman, Juliet Stephenson, David Suchet (Carol Vorderman?).

4. Me in various locations suited to the subject matter: Russian steppes, Hiroshima, Gibraltar, Sicily, up Big Ben, etc.

5. Black-and-white art-house movie à la Kerouac? Fifties beat look, me driving an old Buick, Sophie as beatnik companion with pointy bra, etc.?

6. White studio backdrop. Me on plinth reading poems as they are simultaneously interpreted around me by dance/mime/puppetry.

7. Me on my deathbed as an old man, thinking back over the poems of my life. We flashback to me reading them at various stages of my life. Would need make-up. Am prepared to go to some acting classes if required. (Would this be covered by expenses?)

8. Just my face filling the screen for the whole time, with poems as voice-over.

9. Surreal imagery which is completely at odds with each poem, thus hopefully causing the words to stand out more starkly. For example, during, say, 'Tribute to Justin Wiverly', my poem about a fellow poet, we see footage of penguins/cotton reels/bubbles, etc.

10. A bit daring: how about we film me trying to write a poem? In real time. Show the truth and pain of the creative process? (Not commercial. Also risk factor: cannot guarantee coming up with anything.)

Night Art was a bit of a hangover from the early days of Channel 4, when its schedule didn't consist almost exclusively of cookery programmes, property makeovers and freak shows. It comprised two fifteen-minute programmes each week that explored a diverse range of poetry, music, literature, art and dance. Independent producer Robert Katz had been a regular contributor to the show for five years or so, and was now working on its twelfth series.

ROBERT KATZ: I had initially been booked to do a piece about a man who had spent thirty years studying the art of chimpanzees. Unfortunately, a few days before we were due to start filming one of the chimpanzees had turned on him and all but pulled his face off. It was awful but – and I'm not making light of it – in my time on *Night Art* I had met artists much more volatile than that, so I was used to this kind of unexpected hiccup. By sheer coincidence I had been taken to Hamilton's poetry club 'Word Up' a couple of weeks before. He hadn't really made a massive impact as my cat had just died and my mind was elsewhere but, to tell you the truth, we were pretty stuffed for an alternative subject at such short notice and he seemed as good a last-minute substitute as any. The more I thought about it, though, the more justified I felt in using Hamilton as a replacement for the chimp daubs. I even started getting mildly excited about the possibility of producing what I hoped would be an entertainingly left-field 'Zoetropic album' of an obscure poet's work.

He was very much against the current trend then. Performance poets were the thing at the time: handsome men

in kilts shouting doggerel, not Hamilton's carefully cod-
dled constructions. But that was the attraction of having
him on *Night Art*. We were always in favour of giving space
to stuff you had little or no chance of ever seeing anywhere
else on television.

Hamilton told me that he had missed out on a much
sought-after spot on *The South Bank Show*'s two-part special on YBPs – Young British Poets – having been passed
over for the usual suspects: Simon Armitage, Lavinia
Greenlaw et al., who were storming the cultural landscape
of the nineties, along with their Young British Artist cousins. A researcher from *The South Bank Show* had introduced himself to Hamilton at the beginning of one of the
'Word Up' evenings but was nowhere to be seen come the
interval. So I think Hamilton was a bit raw when we met
in the Fitzroy Tavern on Charlotte Street in May 1999.
Dylan Thomas used to get smashed there, so it seemed
like a good place to start.

Anyway, Hamilton brought some ideas for the visual-
isation of *Shadows of Reflections*. Some were grandiose.
Actually, all were grandiose and some were impossible.
Others were simply bad. As the night went on he started
extemporising, and the ideas he came out with then were
even less feasible. For example, I didn't think we'd be allowed to film on a nuclear submarine even if we could
afford it, and we couldn't. The budget was tiny but Hamilton's expectations were great, and I think it's a tribute
to director Michael Cumming and me that we managed
to show Hamilton in the best light we could, given the
budgetary constraints and the fact that his nerves led to a

crippling bowel complaint which more than once delayed filming.

So, yes, there was a lot riding on this for Hamilton. As far as he was concerned, he was going to stuff Melvyn Bragg and stick two fingers up to LWT. And the strain showed on the first day of filming, when we discovered him snivelling behind a pile of bricks in what is now the King's Cross delta but was then rubble-strewn wasteland. He was fretting over the stresses in a line, the rhythm, the intonation, the volume – everything a poet could fret over. Michael, bless him, told Hamilton to just shout the words very clearly because I'd managed to find us a (cheap) location in the noisiest place in London. But it worked, as you can see.

Then we had some problems with riding a bicycle. He said he could do it and even boasted about 'giving his pals a croggy' when he was a lad. It took seventeen takes (using an expensive jib arm, I might add) to get him to ride exactly ten yards, stop and deliver a short speech to the camera. Fair enough, he had no problem using his mouth, but his legs were like noodles.

Still, when he wasn't causing general inconvenience with something or other related to his gastrointestinal tract, he was very amusing company. His firm belief that he was going to put poetry – and himself – where it belonged kept him going. Something had to, I suppose. Sadly, at the pre-broadcast showing of the piece at Channel Four headquarters he had quite a few glasses of wine over the odds. Not only did he embarrass himself by make a rambling thirty-minute-long speech which didn't make an awful lot of sense but also, at the end of the evening, he staggered up to the Head of Arts Programming and accused her of being 'Ann Widdecombe in a Germaine Greer body suit'. I sort of felt then that just as one door was possibly about to be opened to him, at the very last moment it was instead being reinforced with a good strong Chubb lock to keep him out.

We never worked together again.

SOPHIE: He really was quite dizzy with excitement. He hired a publicist – a foul little man, I seem to remember. As far as Paul was concerned, this was going to change everything. He kept saying, 'I need professional help to manage all the attention. I won't be able to handle it myself.'

PAUL: I've always hated fame. I always will hate fame. That was the one big drawback to this. I was thinking, 'Woah, careful, Hamilton. What if this thing goes off in your face? What if it's suddenly a case of not being able to go anywhere without the staring and the autographs and complete strangers feeling they have the right to come up to you and tell you how great they think you are?' I really had to think long and hard about that. I've seen what fame can do to people. I've met a few famous people. Johnny Hates Jazz come to mind. Charlie and I supported them just after they had their big single. The drummer wouldn't let our drummer use his bass drum and snare. And got a roadie to tell us, too. Classy. I wonder where they are now incidentally?

Then there's Ken Loach. I was collecting for CND in Highgate once, and he passed me. I held the tin out, and without even looking at me he said something like, 'No, I'm just . . .' Well, thanks very much, comrade.

Carol Vorderman. I was talking to her backstage at an Aids benefit, and mid-sentence she just walked off. Just like that. Where did she go? To talk to Alison Moyet by the drinks table. I've got a nine-letter word for you, Carol: politeness.

To be fair, I did once get chatting to George Alagiah in a queue at a petrol station, and he could not have been more pleasant, but, sadly, experience has shown that that is very much an exception to the rule.

Fame. I wouldn't want it if you offered it to me on a silver platter garnished with shining diamonds and a cup of liquid gold with which to wash it down. Fame can only corrupt, turn the ego toxic. What must it be like to live every day obsessed with yourself, thinking about nothing but yourself and what *you* want and what *you* need and what *you're* doing and what *you* say, with the voice in your head always going, 'Me, me, me, me, me, me, me, me, me.'? Jesus.

In the end I was able to dodge all that nonsense. Fortunately, Channel 4 put it out at 11.35 on a Sunday night with no trails, so it was only viewed by the discerning fan, as it were. In retrospect, I had a lucky escape.

I found the programme, 'Paul Hamilton, *Shadows of Reflections*', on YouTube and watched it, as I'd missed it the first time around. I was impressed to what degree, even some fifteen years later, it succinctly sums up Paul and his work, in both style and content. I asked him if he was pleased with it when it was broadcast.

PAUL: At the time I was terribly upset about my hair. I think it was not well managed by the make-up department. I know that sounds on the surface of it rather petty, but I'm nothing if not a perfectionist, so it got in the way of my enjoyment of it a little. It was just kind of a little unkempt in quite a few scenes. I couldn't understand how the producer and director hadn't noticed. I was convinced it was detracting from the poetry. It was fine in a couple of scenes, but that just made it look all the more awry in any scene where it wasn't. Consistency, that's the key to getting it right. But here's the thing: I looked at the show last night for the first time in six months, and it's weird – the hair thing didn't bug me anywhere near as much. Generally I think it's an honest piece of work. I could have quite happily gone on to do more if they'd let me but, you know, this is television. Apparently, on a commercial station it's all about 'ratings' and 'viewing figures' and 'how many people watched it'. At the time I was paranoid that part of the reason Channel 4 didn't want any more was because of my hair. I got some nice feedback, actually. From real people. And they're the ones that count. A lady just down the road stopped me and said she'd enjoyed it. I got a letter from a guy in Burnley. When I asked them, quite a few fellow poets said they'd watched it, which was great to hear.

Paul sent a tape of the programme to several literary agents and poetry publishers, as well as to the producers of *Countdown*.

PAUL: Yes, I suddenly thought, 'Well, raise your game, Hamilton, there's always a seat on dictionary corner, and if they can have Richard Digance, then they can have me.' But, no, they didn't bite. I'm relieved in a way. After my encounter with Carol Vorderman, in hindsight I'm sure I would have been disappointed, and anyway by then Whiteley was no longer at the top of his game. The tape didn't work as far as getting any publishing deal was concerned either. This is the problem. Send them a manuscript, a CD or DVD and it gathers dust for a year and then gets dumped. And you can forget about getting them to come along and see you. Most agents and publishers won't deign to come to your common-or-garden poetry-reading nights. Of course, you'll find a pile of them drooling over Carol Ann Duffy at the Richmond Literature Festival, but you won't find many of them turning up for Johnny or Jane No Mark at the Dog and Bucket in Anywheresville. And in my experience the ones who do drag themselves along are usually so drunk that come the morning they can't remember what it was they saw the night before, let alone whether it was actually any good or not. I'm not judging them, though. They have a tough job. They deserve to unwind at the end of a hard day. Don't we all?

Paul was bitterly disappointed. It seems he'd invested a lot of hope in the Channel 4 outing. After months fruitlessly attempting to capitalise on it he became very depressed. This disappointment and approaching middle age were two major factors that led to Paul's third 'lost' period. As we've seen, there was the lost year after Charlie had gone over to the money men, when Paul had returned to his parents' home. Then there was his lost week spent wandering around some fields in Surrey.

But neither of those unhappy times would come near to matching what he was about to go through.

29

DECAY

PAUL: I suppose my reaction to the lack of any proper appreciation of the Channel 4 programme was just part of a classic mid-life crisis really. I'd turned forty and, I tell you, I wasn't happy about that. For about a year I was doing all the dumb stuff that a lot of guys do when they're in denial about their age and are trying desperately to hold onto their youth.

I bought a pair of leather trousers. They didn't make me feel younger, though. In fact, I'm pretty sure they were responsible for another bout of NSU.

I dyed my hair peroxide blond. That was an error. I looked ridiculous. So the next day I dyed it back to my original colour. The two dyes interacted and I got a tremendously itchy rash right across my scalp. The last time I checked, you're not supposed to suffer from cradle cap at the same time as you start taking sweeteners in your coffee.

In a spirit supposedly of youthful adventurousness I cashed in my premium bonds – not an inconsiderable amount – and invested the proceeds in the dotcom boom, losing the whole lot two months later when the bubble burst.

This was only the first in a series of rapid deflations.

It was around this time that I took my first and last ever Ecstasy tablet. That night I went clubbing with Sophie. The next day she rightly warned me off future entanglements with the drug. Not only had it left me with significantly higher blood pressure, but under its influence my overwhelming sense of affection for everyone I met that night eventually resulted in a fight. Have you ever been punched whilst on Ecstasy? It hurts but you feel very happy about it. I hope the chap who Sophie punched back felt the same way. It wasn't easy for her to get at him. She had to prise me off him first, as I just couldn't stop cuddling him. Or his girlfriend. Or anyone I happened to see really. On our way home, I'm not sure, but I think a street cleaner I embraced threatened to kill me. I couldn't actually hear what he was saying as I was holding him so tightly. It didn't sound friendly, anyway. A warning about Ecstasy: be very careful. I suffered terribly the next day. Appalling diarrhoea and sickness. I guess I was fortunate that some of the pill's effects were dissipated by the tequila and wine I'd had.

Because I was generally feeling quite dowdy I tried changing my whole image. When the rash had cleared, I grew a small ponytail and started dressing a little more street: trainers, baseball cap, tracksuit. I guess I did look kind of cool. I just didn't look like me.

ERIC HAMILTON: First time I saw him in what I call his disc-jockey phase, I nearly died. And I mean really nearly died. Laughed so much I started choking on a liquorice allsort I was eating, and Joan had to get Mr Bird from across the road to come over and perform the Heimlich manoeuvre.

SOPHIE: Oh God, yes. He took the turning forty business really badly. Suddenly it was out with his Craig David

CDs and in with Zombie Nation and Bomfunk MC's. He wasn't fooling me for a second. I remember coming back from the loo in a restaurant and catching him trying to give his number to a waitress who must have been about twenty. I said, 'Paul, she'll think that's the number of the care home you've wandered out of.' I seem to remember he had chocolate mousse all round his mouth.

PAUL: I suppose one of the worst moments was when Sophie noticed my hair was starting to thin on top. I accused her of actually enjoying my descent into decay, as I saw it. I'd already lost a tooth that year, I'd had my first varicose vein and had pulled out well over thirty grey hairs. And not all from my head. I just did not need this news about the possibly approaching spectre of baldness. (This nightmare continued to haunt me until about five years ago, when I realised that I am most probably not going to lose much more hair than I already have. Both my father and grandfathers have high hairlines but, thankfully, none of them ever went 'Gordon Honeycombe'.) I'm afraid I did not take to Sophie's observation very kindly and rather barked at her. She rightly told me not to shoot the messenger. It ended up with me telling her to stop the car and me getting out on the hard shoulder of the M1, just short of junction 28.

Whilst all this was going on there was a more serious concern haunting my every day. The television version of *Shadows of Reflections* had been aired in July of 1999, but here we were almost a year later and I had not written one line of poetry. Not a word, not a syllable. There had not even been the faintest stirring of the ghost of an idea. I had become barren. For the first few months I had not panicked; such compositorial hiati were not uncommon. In fact, there had been a period of nearly two years in the mid-nineties when I had not come up with a single new poem. But the point was that there were always ideas, always the odd line to squirrel away perhaps for later use. In fact, once I stuck together twenty separate lines, none of which I could build on individually, and called the resulting poem 'Frankenrhyme'. It was, I admit, not an easy listen. There was an episode which proved to be an eerie echo of the final scene in Shelley's story, in which the monster is burned by an unthinking mob. At a poetry night in Windsor one evening I was approached after my performance by a bespectacled man who, although not actually carrying a pitchfork, was clearly drunk. He loudly demanded to see my copy of 'Frankenrhyme' and, when I produced it, proceeded to snatch it from me and set fire to it with his cigarette lighter.

Shelley's message was confirmed once again, as it has been so often over the centuries: the mob fears that which flouts conventional form. And often sets fire to it. Well, my answer to that is that you can't set fire to ideas. (Although it's always been a matter of bitter regret that I had not memorised that particular poem, and the copy that was burned was the only one.)

Meanwhile, I began to fear that my very Poet's Essence, too, was lost for ever. Fear begets fear, and my panic heightened.

I sought help. I went to a hypnotherapist. He used a combination of hypnosis, cognitive behavioural therapy and neurolinguistic programming. He unblocked me all right. In just one session. But not in the right way. By the time I had got home I had written fifteen pieces. All limericks. All childishly filthy. They were worthless. And they kept coming. Hundreds a day. I could not stop them. It was like having severe diarrhoea in amphibrachic meter with an AABBA rhyming scheme. I ended up having to pay another £300 for him to block me up again.

I tried Indian head massage. An hour later I got my first-ever migraine.

I went to primal-scream therapy. This induced laryngitis.

Finally, in desperation, and against all my instincts as a logical pragmatist, I went to a healer recommended by one of Sophie's friends. A pleasant elderly lady called Jean laid a hand on my forehead in her living room in Hendon and kept gently shushing me, even though I wasn't saying anything. Still nothing. Although I do feel it's only fair to report that a rather nasty recurring case of athlete's foot mysteriously cleared up completely overnight. And hasn't returned since. Coincidence? I honestly do not know.

Just once I thought that I had broken the impasse when a poem spilled onto a piece of paper late one night. I was so ecstatically relieved that I had a good few whiskies in celebration. But in the cold light of day, to my dawning horror, I read my new poem and saw that it seemed familiar in some way. I showed it to Sophie. Did it ring any bells? After studying it intently for a minute or so she started laughing and did not stop. Eventually I got it from her that I had, all but word for word, set down the lyrics of a Bay

City Rollers song. It is irrelevant which one. I was utterly mortified. I had always despised the Bay City Rollers, with their ridiculous image and their cynical violation of rock and roll. I shudder now to think that those facile lyrics had lain in my mind like some pestilential time bomb, waiting for the right time to make their awful appearance and utterly rob me of any hope. Proof, surely, of the fact that we should always be aware that, in one form or another, great evil is in us all.

It is hard to write what I am about to write now.

It is no excuse that I was hung-over.

It is no excuse that I thought my life as a poet was finished.

It is no excuse that all reason and control had abandoned me.

As Sophie sat on the divan, eyes wet with tears of mirth, I did something I will be ashamed of until the day I die.

I hit myself in front of a woman.

Again and again I blindly struck out until, dimly, through the white noise of my frenzy, I heard Sophie's screams begging me to stop. Eventually I heeded them, and all became deathly silent as I stood swaying in dazed horror. In my head a terrible voice was taunting me, 'Look what you have become. Look what you have become.'

30

ESCAPE

PAUL: I ran headlong from the house and did not stop until the breath was ragged in my lungs and I had fallen sobbing against an empty grit dispenser somewhere in Archway.

I don't know how long I was there. Maybe twenty minutes, maybe three-quarters of an hour, but gradually my sobbing eased, my tears dried. I felt strangely clear, almost serene. But it was the serenity of the void. I wasn't who I thought I was any more. I wasn't a poet. I wasn't Sophie's boyfriend. I wasn't anybody. And I knew what I was going to do. I was going to walk away from it all. Just like that. That very day. I went back to the flat to throw a few things into a bag, have a quick bath and return my library book, because as far as I was concerned I would not be back. That done, I got on the Tube and, without thinking, found myself an hour or so later at Paddington station. It was strange. I felt a new direction. The direction of no direction. I would look at the destination board and I would get on the train to the first town or city I saw. I looked up and my eyes alighted on 'Maidenhead' rendered in orange neon. Maidenhead, Berkshire. I would get on a train to Maidenhead in Berkshire. I would go to Maidenhead in Berkshire. And that was my interminable mantra in those dark hours: 'I am going to Maidenhead in Berkshire. Maidenhead in Berkshire. Maidenhead in Berkshire.'

Round and round in my mind. 'Maidenhead in Berkshire.' I was broken.

It wasn't just Paul that was broken. Cracks had already been forming in his relationship with Sophie. She takes up the story.

SOPHIE: I must say, Paul and I have had a lot of ups and downs in our time together, but this was the downest of all the downs. We'd been off the boil for over a year really. It all started when he got involved with that Channel 4 thingy. There was the all-day writing and then the all-evening rewriting, followed by the all-night re-rewriting. He was obsessed. And then there were a couple of reviews in the papers about the programme. He only saw one, thank God. The 'laughably shallow pretentiousness' one. I don't know what would have happened if he'd seen the bad one. On top of all that there was his block, the haemorrhoids, the impotence, the leg twitches . . . I mean, it just didn't stop. I felt so sorry for the poor old love, but also I'd started to feel rather neglected. It's queer how thin that line is, isn't it? You know, the one between the sexiness of a tortured artist and the God Almighty turn-off of a snivelling wretch. So when Edmund came along, well, maybe he was just what I needed at the time.

Edmund Rogers was a widowed sweet-shop owner who had called at Sophie and Paul's flat one evening while canvassing on behalf of the Lib Dems. When Sophie answered the door, he hadn't even introduced himself before he noticed that she was crying. Paul and Sophie had had another row that afternoon, and Paul had stormed out to sulk at a matinee showing of *If* at Islington's Screen on the Green cinema. Being a generally kind soul and one of those people you instantly feel at ease with, it wasn't long before Edmund was sitting on the sofa in the flat, listening to Sophie pour her heart out about Paul and his increasingly difficult ways.

SOPHIE: It all started from there really. Edmund was such a good listener. And although he was in his sixties, he was still quite good-looking in a Peter Sissons sort of way. Anyway, it wasn't his looks I fell for. It was his kindness. It was such a welcome change from Paul and his tantrums. I mean, that morning he went properly bonkers and started duffing himself up. I thought, 'Oh, Sophie, what are you doing with this colossal chump?' I mean, I've seen Paul lose it before. He had a full-blown panic attack when a giraffe stuck its nose through the car window at West Midlands Safari Park. Started hitting it with a baguette. And he was screaming. Screaming like a woman. A warden got involved and there was talk of charging him with assault. I don't know. Would that stand up in court? Assaulting a giraffe? Anyway, they never followed it up, thank goodness. And he's never been a monarchist, but he was inconsolable on the day of Diana's funeral. He was hyperventilating at one point. And I'll never forget him throwing the radio through a window when Edwina Currie was on *Desert Island Discs*. But this was a new level. I mean, he was socking himself in the jaw. Banging his head against the wall. Punching himself in the legs. Then, when he came to, he had such a look on his face. I thought to myself, 'Oh dear. Cuckoo!' And then he just bolted like a hare. I remember thinking, 'Well, big blue balls to all this.' Something just led me to go mooching round to Edmund's shop. He could see how upset I was, so he closed early and we went for a walk in the park while I told him the latest. We ended up back at his and he invited me to stay for dinner. Steak and kidney pie and mash with baby carrots and peas. Peach yoghurt for afters. All washed down with a couple of very reasonable bottles of Malbec. And then from that to *Inspector Linley* it was just a short hop to bed. It all seemed so natural. And after Paul and all his nonsense, so easy.

31

MAIDENHEAD (LIMBO NUMBER 3)

In October of 2000 Paul arrived in Maidenhead to begin the third of his lost periods. This one was to last nearly three years.

PAUL: I often think back to that time and try to quantify where exactly I was mentally and emotionally. If I were to try to describe it, I suppose I felt like I was removed from everything. I was Major Tom. I was Robinson Crusoe. I was, in a sense, Johnny Hates Jazz.

It was a featureless detachment. I felt like I had taken a Mogadon before being put into a diving suit wrapped in cotton wool, which had then been immersed in quick-drying cement, the whole solid, senseless block then being buried somewhere on the Isle of Man.

In a daze I alighted from the train carriage at Maidenhead railway station. In a daze I rented a tiny studio flat. In a daze I answered an ad for a 'base' guitarist for a covers band. And in a daze I took out most of the money from my Abbey National savings account and bought a cheap Dean Edge Series bass guitar with EMG pickups and a Behringer BX108 Thunderbird bass amplifier. The only answer seemed to lie in being lost in music. I had had absolutely nothing to do with music or bands since my days with Charlie. I knew it was a step back but the way ahead was literally blocked. And as for sideways moves? They're for crabs.

I got the gig. It seemed my fingering still impressed. The band was called The Soundalikes. A breach of the Trade Descriptions Act, in that they managed to sound nothing at all like any of the bands or singers whose songs they covered.

The Soundalikes were comprised of a drummer called Neil, a cheery simpleton who lived on benefits on the eighteenth floor of a condemnable block of flats; a lead guitarist called Greg, a mediocre talent with an extraordinary ego who despised the singer; and Nigel, the singer and rhythm guitarist, a barrel-chested, mulleted, mountain of a man who took the whole thing very seriously indeed. And who, incidentally, despised the lead guitarist right back.

They mostly ignored me. And that suited me just fine. Pubs, bars, weddings, birthdays, anniversaries, you name it, The Soundalikes would turn up, set up, usually in some cramped corner, and proceed to deliver rough approximations of the most well-known songs by any number of guitar-based bands from any given year since 1955. The Kinks? We could give you most of the day and some of the night. T. Rex? We'd almost get it on. Oasis? Well, we could at least serve up a Pomagne Supernova.

For three years I ranged through the Maidenhead/Slough area: Marlow, Burnham, Twyford, Hambleden, Fawley, Rotherfield Peppard, Rotherfield Greys – we played them all and, to me, they all just blurred into one badly lit room full of drunks asking if we did 'Angels'. Which wasn't really a Soundalikes kind of number. But which we did anyway. Moderately well.

SOPHIE: Neither of us tried to contact the other really. There was a letter from Paul about a week after that awful scene. All terribly emotional. Something about him wanting me to try to forget him, and that he was going to do the same. Forget himself, that is. I was quite cross. And, of course, hurt as well. And so I did what I've always done in that situation: I got married. I hadn't been married for quite a while, so it seemed about time. Paul was always dead against marriage. He said he didn't need a piece of paper to sanctify our relationship. I think he just didn't want our mummies and daddies to meet. Anyway, I married Edmund. I proposed actually. He was quite shocked. He said he wasn't really ready, that he was still in mourning for his wife. I must admit there were quite a few pictures of her around the place. But I talked him round. Of course, I know now we were both on the rebound. I realised that there was something not quite right about a month after the honeymoon, when I went into his shed at the bottom of the garden. He used to spend a fair bit of time there. Called it his 'quiet place'. Well, anyway, one day, when he was at work, I got the key and let myself in. Inside there was a mannequin wearing a pinny standing at an ironing board, with a photo of his wife's face stuck on the front of its head. I suppose people deal with grief in different ways. Anyway, we had a chat that evening and agreed that perhaps we'd both been a little hasty.

I asked Paul whether he was still trying to write poetry during this time.

PAUL: You don't understand. I had closed down. My emotions – anything to do with feeling – were in some kind of suspended animation. For instance, sometimes the arguments between Greg and Nigel would get quite violent. I remember once, at a gig at Hambleden tennis club, Nigel had given Greg such a filthy look for forgetting the key change in 'The More I See You' that Greg threw a fuzz pedal at him. It hit me straight in the testicles. It didn't even register. *Nada.*

On another occasion, at a roofer's wedding in Oakley Green, the best man, out of his mind on overpriced lager, thought it hugely amusing to push a plate of trifle into my face while we were in the middle of a song. I didn't miss a note. And we were playing 'House of the Rising Sun' at the time. Tricky bass line. I didn't even wipe the trifle off. I woke up the next morning with it still on my face. There were probably traces visible a month later.

I had many an offer from ladies at gigs. It seemed that the mysterious bass man with the faraway look had a certain appeal. I acquiesced to some of the more persistent come-hithers. More out of a sense of resigned weariness than anything else. But even in the middle of the act of love I would sadly look down upon myself, mechanically going through the motions, like a seal trying vainly to manoeuvre itself off a dry rock.

Sophie, meanwhile, was far from depressed.

SOPHIE: I kept 'Word Up' going. I even expanded it. Put on a regular burlesque night, a Scrabble evening and speed dating for pensioners, though the speed dating was a bit of a flop really – they never seemed to get past talking about the weather before it was time to move on to the next person.

You'd've thought I would have been put off relation-ships, wouldn't you, but after Edmund I got hitched an-other two times while Paul and I were separated. There was the French minister of transport I met at Lord Bath's summer ball. That was a non-starter. You see, typical Fren-chie, he was an absolute head-in-the-clouds romantic. In fact, that's what attracted me to him in the first place. It was '*l'amour*' this and '*l'amour*' that. Trouble is, on our wedding night, after making wonderful love for hours on a bed of lilacs in a fabulous suite in Versailles he told me that it was impossible for us to ever know such joy again and so it was only right that we should take our own lives together. Can you believe it? Kept trying to make me jump out of the window with him. In the end I pushed him out on his own. Broke both his legs. Shame really. He had some terrific moves. Then, after a quickie divorce, I plunged straight back into party-girl mode. A few months later I got together with a really gorgeous actor, Peter, who was also recently divorced. After a whirlwind romance I married him. Part of what reeled me in were these won-derful anecdotes he had. He'd tell me these amazing sto-ries about terribly amusing incidents that had happened to him while he was acting. For instance, once he had been doing a 'telly', a job in television, and the script called for him to walk into a room and hang his coat up on a coat hook. Well, every time he went to hang his coat up it fell on the floor. Peter was getting more and more anxious and worked up about it until finally, after about ten 'takes', the director said to him, 'All right, we'll lose the coat, darling. Let's just agree that your character doesn't feel the cold!'

Thing was, though, after about six months of blissful happiness I realised that Peter only had about twenty or so anecdotes, and once he'd told me them all he started repeating them. It didn't matter that I'd hint that I'd heard them before, he'd just plough on to the end regardless. Some of them were very long. The longest one was seventeen minutes. I timed it once. Something about Trevor Eve and a tuna sandwich. Unfortunately, Peter hit a bit of a slow patch after we got married, apart from two days on something called *The Bill*, so he didn't have a chance to collect any new anecdotes. I stuck with it as long as I could but I literally walked out on him in the end. We were at a dinner party with some of his actor friends. I'd heard most of their anecdotes too. I used to dread those dos. Anyway, an actress was telling the one about the alcoholic director who'd been pushed into a duck pond by Helen Mirren, again, and I just couldn't take any more. I slipped out without any of them noticing and walked all the way home from Muswell Hill. It was on the way home that I started to realise that I really did miss Paul. By the time I'd got to Tufnell Park I'd decided that enough was enough. I got home, packed a bag and took a taxi to a hotel. The next morning I called Paul's mother for the first time since the split. She was pretty worried about him, poor thing. He'd only called her once in the last year or so and he'd sounded pretty low. She didn't have a number or an address. All she could tell me was that he was living in Maidenhead, was playing in a band called The Sandy Bikes and that she and Eric had just had to pay out £2,000 to combat rising damp in the utility room.

I thought, 'Right, Hamilton, I may have little or nothing to go on but I'm bringing you in.'

Sophie's ensuing search for Paul is the stuff of true romance. What follows is my own presentation of the events up to and including the reunion. Although involving a certain amount of artistic licence, it is nevertheless based entirely on Paul's and Sophie's memories as related by them to me.

32

SEARCHING

Maidenhead at this time was a depressing place, its drab grey post-war architecture only slightly overshadowed by its drabber greyer pre-war architecture. As Sophie walked out of the train station she found herself suddenly realising just how difficult a task she had set herself. What if The Sandy Bikes only rarely did gigs? Was it even necessarily the case that they would advertise the ones they did? What if they'd split up?

The first thing was to find somewhere to stay. The Novotel near the station would do. Nothing too grand. This was no holiday.

Sophie started the search by scouring the entertainment pages of the local newspapers. The *Maidenhead Mercury*: nothing. The *Maidenhead Evening News*: nothing. The *Maidenhead Courier*: nothing. The *Maidenhead Messenger*, *Gazette*, *Journal* and *Post*: nothing.

After drinking a UHT-milk-infused cup of tea she took a brief nap and then headed into the Maidenhead night for an initial foray.

Nothing.

Paul had come to the right place to be forgotten. A man can lose himself in Maidenhead. And it seems he had.

Over the next week Sophie went to every live music venue in the Maidenhead area she could find and made enquiries. In each case not only had they never booked a band called The Sandy Bikes, they'd never actually heard of them. A visit to a local talent agency drew a similar blank. By the following Monday she was at her wit's end.

Deadlock.

She had followed every possible lead.

In her growing sense of helplessness it then occurred to her that perhaps Paul had told his mother he was in Maidenhead when he was in fact in Marlow or Beaconsfield. God, he could be in Eton Wick for all she knew.

She widened the search, taking in Cookham, Holyport, High Wycombe and Gerrards Cross. The same blank stares. The same shaking heads. She knew the depths of her desperation when, finally, she found herself vainly looking for music venues in Stoke Poges.

Returning to her lonely hotel room, she sat mulling over the sad conclusion that Paul and she were lost to each other. She would leave the next morning and start accepting that he was out of her life for ever. Meanwhile, there was a bar downstairs. Time to drown her sorrows. Who knew, perhaps there was someone down there she could marry.

It was a Saturday night. The bar was full of the usual disparate groups of assorted guests: a band of portly Red Dwarf enthusiasts attending a convention; a group of thirty-something men on a stag weekend; a number of middle-aged businessmen with their red-faced mistresses; a gaggle of pensioners belonging to the University of the Third Age bound for the Twyford Downs. It was now past eleven and the separate pockets of woozy, boozy bonhomie were merging into a single miasma of steadily increasing uproar. Sophie sat at the bar, still and alone amidst the slack-faced men and women, all of whom seemed to be enjoying the same huge joke.

Coming back from the toilet she passed a set of double doors over which was the legend 'Connaught Suite'. From inside she could hear the hum and thud of music. Suddenly the doors burst open and she was nearly knocked over by a young woman with luminously orange skin and a dress to match, who was immediately followed by a silver-suited young man of the same age with shark-fin hair and designer stubble.

The young lady rounded on her pursuer.

'Fuck off, Robbie!' she shrieked.

'Babe . . .'

She thrust her face close into his, eyes screwed shut.

'Fuck off!'

The young man grabbed her wrist.

'I wasn't kissin' her! She just came at me, babe!'

'Let go!'

'She's mental, babe!'

'Fuckin' let go!'

'No, I fuckin' won't!'

Sophie loomed over them both.

'Language, darlings,' she said.

They snapped their heads towards her and, as one, snarled, 'Fuck off!'

She was about to do just that when she glanced into the room. Three long tables covered with heavily stained white tablecloths were positioned around three sides of the room, each laden with half-empty glasses, paper plates, napkins and assorted detritus. In the space in front of the tables wedding guests, ranging from hysterically overexcited children running round at full pelt to pleasantly squiffy octogenarians, were enjoying the music of a four-piece band lined up against the fourth wall. The band in question were competently churning out a version of 'Hi Ho Silver Lining'. She noted the name of the band on the bass drum. In the middle of the throng the happy couple were singing along to the chorus, punching the air whilst clinging onto each other for dear life.

'Well, I hope your marriage lasts longer than mine tend to,' Sophie mumbled to herself, and then she turned, stepped around the couple, who were now kissing extravagantly, and walked down the corridor back towards the bar.

She ordered a nightcap. A large one. As she nursed her drink, the chatter of the drinkers in the bar now becoming cacophonous, she suddenly felt a nagging sensation she couldn't explain. She tried to shake it off. What was it? The arguing couple? No. The name of the band, The Soundalikes? No. She raised the tumbler to her lips and then froze. The . . . Sounda . . . the Sandy . . . THE SANDY BIKES. Brain pounding, she sat perfectly still for a moment, then she downed her drink in one, slid off her bar stool and practically ran back to the Connaught Suite.

The formerly warring couple had moved to a chair just to the side of the doors and were now engaged in an activity not entirely appropriate for a hotel corridor. She slipped into the function room. The band was still playing. 'Born to Be Wild' now. Reasonably well. The place was going crazy. Sophie scanned the band's faces. She stopped.

And so did her heart. There he stood. Paul. Staring blankly out, slightly apart from the rest of the group, mechanically plucking at his bass strings. Sophie had never seen anyone look so utterly alone. She gingerly made her way through the guests, dodging reeling uncles, gyrating cousins, hand-jiving grandmothers and a collapsed niece. At the front a large woman of about sixty, impressively inebriated, was trying to catch Paul's attention as she jumped and gyrated and wobbled a large pair of breasts, the top halves of which were spilling from a very low-cut dress. Behind her a couple of equally paralytic friends were laughingly egging her on. He seemed totally oblivious. Sophie neatly sidestepped the loose-limbed lunge of the best man and finally came to a halt beside the large woman. And there Sophie stood, perfectly still in the seething, whooping mass, looking impassively at Paul. The large woman accidentally bumped into her once. Twice. After the third time, Sophie swung her hips very hard to her left, sending the large woman and her two friends cannoning into five other people, all of whom then toppled over into a shrieking, cackling heap of hilarity. Paul's eyes flickered briefly towards the commotion and then onto Sophie's face as she stood motionless, staring at him. Unseeing at first, realisation dawned. Slowly he stopped playing. As the band thundered on Paul and Sophie stood stock-still among the hot press of floundering bodies, eyes locked. Time stopped.

33

FINDING

PAUL: Well, eventually she just walked up to me, took my bass guitar off and leaned it against the amp. I'll never forget the band's faces. You know, 'What the hell is going on here?' She took my hand and led me out of the room, through the bar, upstairs to her room and straight into bed.

There is good sex and then there is sex that transcends. I think that's the kind of sex Sophie experienced that night. I too was transported. For hours we lost ourselves in each other, often barely able to carry on for weeping, and other times nearly having to stop because we were laughing so very much. When I awoke in the morning I felt strangely reborn. I suppose, to be completely accurate, I felt strangely re-reborn in that I'd felt strangely reborn after my week living in the barn. It depends on your starting point. But then again, doesn't everything?

The most wonderful moment in all this came when, on that Sunday morning, 18 September 2003, Sophie was in the toilet and I, feeling as if I were outside myself, took a piece of hotel notepaper and a pencil and wrote my first new poem in four and a half years. I think it is the most truthful poem I have ever written. Perhaps I'll never write another poem as truthful as that. Then let it be so. At least I've written that one. It is called 'Writer's Block' and its simple honesty still moves me deeply (see page 243).

Re-establishing contact with Sophie and writing a new poem seems to have completely revitalised Paul in all areas of his life.

PAUL: I went on a big health kick. I'd been drinking far too much. I gave up alcohol. I gave up meat completely. I started doing yoga, and that led to my interest in meditation. It was a massive change in lifestyle and attitude. A revolution. One evening, though, at dinner, I looked at Sophie's lamb chops and bottle of Merlot and then at my Linda McCartney sausages and glass of elderflower cordial and I crumbled.

I have absolutely no regrets. At the end of those five days of kindness to myself I felt utterly revitalised.

I started getting into all kinds of new things. Ice-skating. Bird-watching. I went to tap-dancing lessons. I even took up the bassoon for a while. And before too long ideas for new poems started coming, and then actual new poems. Since then I've never really looked back.

Incidentally, if any of you guys from The Soundalikes are reading this, I can't really apologise for walking out on you that night. I'm not sure Nelson Mandela apologised to his wardens when he finally walked out of the Robben Island prison. Because although The Soundalikes was absolutely where I had to be at that particular time in my life, it was a kind of prison. I didn't really want to be in a golf-club bar on New Year's Eve playing songs by Status Quo. It was never my intention to end up spending my Saturday nights in Rotary clubs picking out the bass line to 'Song Sung Blue'. But, hey, guys, as screws go, you were all right, and I mean that. Let me just say two things, though. Firstly, to Greg. Greg, OK, so you think Nigel is a 'fat, talentless prick', but that doesn't actually make him evil, does it? I mean, does it? Think about that. And when you've thought about it, think about it again.

And secondly, to Nigel. Nigel, even if you could actually scientifically prove that Greg is 'a whining little wanker with his head stuck so far up his arse it's coming out of his neck again' (and that's a bloody tall order), let me put it to you that even if you could prove that, he would still rank as a human being. In fact, I'd like to venture that that is in fact a no-brainer. You two are very alike, you know, and that's the problem. I hope that one day, instead of focusing on the things that tear you apart, you can both find the wisdom to capitalise on the things you have in common. I wish you all the luck in the world.

34

MAKING RADIO WAVES

The next four years saw Paul returning to very good form. He went back to making regular live appearances and slowly but surely worked his way back to his pre-Maidenhead yearly average of two to three new poems a year.

In 2007 BBC Radio 4 producer Ann White approached Paul with an offer to showcase his talents.

ANN WHITE: When I first encountered Paul Hamilton I had only been working in the Radio 4 poetry and spoken-word department for about six months. I thought the whole department needed a major shake-up. I mean, yes, there is an argument for the infallibility of the Super Seven – Donne, Keats, Kipling, Eliot, Plath, Heaney and Duffy, with, of course, an occasional snippet of Zephaniah to add a little exotica – but I thought we could afford to widen the brief.

One day at a departmental strategy meeting I brought up the idea that perhaps we should be looking to include newer, younger poets. It was not well received. When I pointed out that Keats was only twenty-four when he wrote 'Ode to a Nightingale', the argument came back, 'Yes, but he's dead.'

I decided to persevere and took it upon myself to start going to poetry readings in search of new talent. One evening I went to this little place in North London somewhere and saw Paul. I was immediately struck by how sincere his poetry was. I hadn't experienced such sincerity for a long, long time. True, it was a little rough around the edges, but it was very, very sincere.

By now I realised that engaging in a departmental debate about new types of programmes was futile. The long-established modus operandi was that old programmes were essentially reassembled and presented as new. My solution was to quite simply make Paul's programme without anyone realising what was going on. I worked so quickly that in a flurry of administrative and bureaucratic corner-cutting the entire commissioning and development process took just seventeen months, and by the summer of 2007 we were ready to start recording the first of four fifteen-minute programmes called *Poets' Tree.*

It was an interesting process, let's just say that. I don't think Paul realised just what a revolutionary step was being taken in commissioning his programme, and that I was personally sticking my neck out somewhat. And quite often he wanted to push the envelope perhaps a little too far for my liking.

PAUL: Well, it was quite an experience. For a start, I was surprised that Radio 4 would be interested in me. I think when it comes down to it I'm perhaps not quite cosy enough for them. I'm afraid I don't have a lot of time for Radio 4 as a station. OK, the *Today* programme is reasonable, and *Midweek* with Libby Purves has some great guests. And they do broadcast some terrific drama; the writing and acting are consistently first class. And it has to be said that *The Now Show* goes from strength to strength as far as satirical bite and sheer laugh-out-loud funniness goes. But I find the rest of its content . . . well, shall we just say it errs a little too far towards the middle-class? Nevertheless, I liked Ann. She was pretty straightforward. But the whole thing nearly didn't happen. When it came to discussing what kind of programme we were going to make, we had quite a few arguments. I guess I should have expected caution in the face of a sense of adventure: ideas such as the appreciation of the beauty of the innate poetry in the uncensored outpourings of a homeless meths drinker; the editing of the words of Tony Blair so that he appeared to boast of being a war criminal in rhyming couplets; a poem by Justin Wiverly imagining a graphic sexual encounter between Mother Teresa and Richard Dawkins. Back would come the answers to anything even vaguely challenging: 'We shouldn't,' 'We mustn't,' 'We can't.'

Having said that, I still got some stuff through that I was very proud of. It was important to me that the programme be about poetry as a whole rather than just about me. And so it ended up being a mixture of my poetry, my interviews with other poets, me reading other people's poetry and my thoughts in general about various examples of poetry.

A highlight, in my opinion, was my interview with a prostitute, in which I encouraged her to write a poem about her life as a sex worker. This was to illustrate my long-held belief that everyone is a poet. Some may be better than others, but that essential truth remains.

We gave her a couple of hours to see what she could come up with. She was very sceptical that she would be able to produce anything of quality. My argument was and is that truth is quality. And her poem contained that one essential element: truth. Here it is. Judge for yourselves.

MY JOB

Sometimes my job feels really really silly
'Cos a man comes to me and he gets out his willy.
Then he puts it in my fanny for a minute or so,
Then he gives me fifty pounds and it's time for him to go.

That is what I call pure verse.

Another wonderful moment occurred when I visited my former English teacher, Mr Jackson, then in his late eighties, in a care home in Gillingham. It was wonderful to be able to repay a debt of gratitude to the man who, though I didn't realise it at the time, was majorly instrumental in planting the seed of awareness of the power and truth of poetry. He has since passed away, and as a tribute to him I'd like to reproduce the poem of thanks I wrote for him and which I read to him during the course of an interview for episode three. He was virtually speechless after listening to it and I would say that without doubt that was one of the most moving moments of my life. Mr Jackson always maintained that poetry was for listening to as well as reading. A point I heartily concur with. Please note that this should be read aloud with an awareness that of all my poems this is the one that most nakedly owes a debt of gratitude to urban rap.

THANK YOU, MR JACKSON

*Thank you, Mr Jackson, for the fury and the passion, for the
utter dedication to the power of the word.*
*Thank you, Mr Jackson, for causing a reaction, for the
truthful interaction and the wonder that you stirred.*
*Thank you, Mr Jackson, for all your stimulation to use im-
agination in the baring of my soul.*
*Thank you, Mr Jackson, for making me take action to make
my destination the Poetry Goal.*
Thank you, Mr Jackson.
Thank you, Mr Jackson.
Thank you, Mr Jackson.
Thank you, Mr Jackson.

I remain indebted to Ann White for pointing me in
the direction of some poetry I may well never have come
across without her say-so. (I should point out that this
was the only time, purely for the sake of the programme,
that I have ever reneged on my avowed avoidance of exposure to other poets' work. It was a painful sacrifice but
one that I knew I had to make for my listeners.) One of
the most heart-rending poems I have ever read was an
early nineteenth-century poem by Jake Hobbes. We all
think we have it tough these days, don't we? 'Oh, I ordered
my curry delivery an hour ago and it's still not here.' 'Oh,
I've been cut off from the call centre.' 'Oh, my auntie has
died.' Well, what about this to stuff your guff?

THE LAMENT OF JENNY ABLE

And away he did march my fine handsome man
In the year eighteen hundred and four.
Left me alone with our eight bonny bairns,
Hungry and broken and poor.
And long did I labour out in the cold fields,
And each year the crop it did fail,
And my fingers did bleed as I shivered and shook
In the wind and the snow and the hail.

Then came a young sergeant into our town
Said, 'Where is the wife of John Able?'
'Here, sir!' I cried, and he said, 'John has died.
And left you but nought for your table.'

And I wept bitter tears as the bairns they all cried,
Empty and sorrowed and starving.
But what could I do, a poor woman alone
With nary a solitary farthing?

And then did some thieves steal my hens and my goat,
And ere I could properly mourn.
Down came that miserable hovel of mine,
Crushed by a terrible storm.

Then came the plague and it swept through our town
And carried away my poor mites.
And I buried them all with own bleeding hands
And lay awake grieving at nights.

Then did some men from the town do me wrong,
Like beasts did they use me for shame.

And so did I vow to take my own life,
So much had they sullied my name.

And so from a tree did I hang my poor self
But yet there is more I must tell.
With a crack of dire thunder, the earth split asunder
And I tumbled below into hell!

Now the flames they do burn as they lick at my soul
And the demons do tear at my flesh.
And just when I cry I could not feel more pain,
Then they start all their tortures afresh.

And I scream and I howl and I groan and I moan
And I shriek and I wail and I yell.
And here I shall stay till the end of all time
In the depths of this terrible hell.
In the depths, in the depths, in the hot, stinking depths,
In the depths of this terrible hell.
In the depths, in the depths, in the depths, in the depths,
dreadful depths of this terrible hell!

Whenever I read that poem I always feel a little spring return to my step.

Also, happy to pass on the word, I was honoured to include a poem, now sadly out of print, by one of Justin Wiverly's favourite poets, the little known and hugely underrated fifties beat poet Alex Hurwich. Hurwich, incidentally, was a contemporary and one-time lover of Lenny Coggs, who dropped into 'Word Up' on a number of memorable occasions.

DWAYNE O'REILLY'S ASS

Ass of magic, ass of disguise,
Ass of mystery beneath cobalt skies.
Ass that sat on hungry faces,
Ass enjoyed by all God's races.
Jade ass spits potato chips.
Ass-wipe joy, and ass-wipe lips,
Ass of wonder, ass of might,
Ass of royal beauty bright.

At Rushmore I asked to have an ass
Like beautiful Dwayne O'Reilly's ass.
All the presidents there were stoned
And, stoned, they groaned and this intoned:
'Dwayne Reilly's ass may be a gas
But ask not what you can do for your ass,
Ask what your ass can do for you.
Wop bop a loo bop, a wop bam boo.'

During the making of *Poets' Tree* at Radio 4, at the very heart of the Establishment, Paul found himself witness to workplace behaviour that shocked him to the core.

PAUL: I saw and experienced things during my time at Broadcasting House that I never would have expected to encounter. Not there. Almost anywhere else, sure, but not there. I guess I thought that Radio 4 was a bastion of middle-class convention. Sure, maybe a little right-wing, but only in an Edward Heath kind of way. I went there expecting to witness dignified decency thriving in a general atmosphere of polite geniality. What I did not expect was to walk into a pit of widespread drug abuse and unbridled sexual promiscuity.

On my very first visit I saw the obvious signs of cocaine use in the *Woman's Hour* studio, and an hour later inadvertently interrupted a newsreader 'giving headlines' to his producer in the microphone cupboard. I began to wonder if I hadn't stumbled upon some sort of modern-day Sodom. I had my bottom pinched no less than three times by three different people there, one of whom is still quite high up in the religious affairs department. I witnessed a continuity announcer, quite clearly in his cups, being helped into his sound booth and slapped into consciousness seconds before going on air. And this was at ten o'clock in the morning. In the canteen one day I got talking to a producer from the drama department. She ended our conversation with a whispered suggestion that I come to her office at half past six, when everyone had gone home, because, as she put it, she had a part for me she'd love to see me get my teeth into. She was seventy if she was a day. I saw joints openly smoked on the roof terrace, and once, when the lift doors opened, I won't tell you what I saw Melvyn Bragg and Martha Kearney doing. You could not make it up. I've certainly never listened to Radio 4 since without wondering just what act of uninhibited hedonism is actually taking place somewhere just behind that genteel facade.

Poets' Tree attracted fairly low listening figures and no reviews, and consequently was not recommissioned for another series.

PAUL: Oh God, they didn't get it. Of course they didn't. No problemo. As far as I was concerned I sneaked in there, did a little guerrilla work and then sneaked out. I don't think they knew what hit them.

It's their good fortune that I'm not the vindictive type. The tales I could tell. I still have dreams. Some of the things I saw. I'm talking to you, Michael Buerk. Moral maze indeed.

35

UP TO NOW

Since 2007 Paul has continued to regularly perform his poetry and host the 'Word Up' club in North London. He has a monthly slot, *Paul Hamilton's Poetry Clinic*, on digital radio station Radio Verse where listeners are invited to send their poetry in so that Paul can give 'as much positive feedback as is realistically possible'. He also offers a fortnightly poetry workshop to violent young offenders at a detention centre, a project which, while continuing to have its teething problems, is nevertheless one he is determined to persevere with.

In 2008 he and Sophie split for six months after he decided to adopt celibacy in an attempt to 'give a fresh angle' to his poetry. The result was that he developed a kidney infection, leading to a renewed bout of NSU so severe that he was hospitalised for a week. Meanwhile, Sophie met and married an Austrian ski instructor. True to form it wasn't very long before that marriage, as Sophie laughingly comments, 'went very much downhill'. Her and Paul's last separation occurred in 2010, after an argument about the whereabouts of a television remote control. It lasted just two months.

Both are now convinced that they will spend the rest of their lives together.

SOPHIE: Marriage? Oh, I'm sure that'll happen at some point. There's no avoiding it. Written in the stars! Not to

Paul, of course. Oh no. Kiss of death. It'll be to some silly bugger after Paul and I have had some ludicrous spat about salad dressing or the EU or something. It'll last about a week and that'll be that. Marriage is my fatal flaw, you see. Every now and then I've just suddenly thrown every bit of common sense to the wind and, usually after a few glasses of giggles, gone and got hitched to some poor wretch or other. You never know, though. Perhaps my marrying days are finally over. But even if they're not, Paul knows and I know that I'll always come back to him. Because of what he is.

And what is he?

SOPHIE: He's a silly sausage, that's what he is. But he's my silly sausage.

PAUL: We've loved, we've hated. We've liked, we've been indifferent. We've experimented sexually to such a degree that we've actually come back round to the missionary position. We've fought. We've shouted. We've whispered and we've sung. We've wept. We've laughed. We've eaten and we've drunk. And through it all we've loved. All this despite the fact that, waiting in the wings, there has always been a demanding mistress who has ruled my head, my heart and my genitals. And that mistress is Lady Poetry. Both a blessing and a curse. Both wings and chains. It is my great good fortune that Sophie has borne my infatuation with grace and dignity. Sophie, thank you for understanding.

And what now?

PAUL: You know what? I'm not going to say much about that. Because it's just talk, isn't it? And I'm more interested in action than endless chatter. So let me just say this: I'll keep going. I have to keep going because, here's the thing, I don't actually know when to stop. I never have. And I don't think I ever will. Because I've got something to say. And that something is: I am a poet.

SHADOWS OF REFLECTIONS

Finally, and fittingly, to end I am more than chuffed to present to you the 2014 version of Shadows of Reflections *by Paul Hamilton. It's been more than twenty years in the forming and, I think, well worth the wait. It features many of the poems Paul originally intended to include in the collection when he first came up with the idea in 1995. The bonus is that this present-day version includes several poems he has written more recently.*

For all the rows we've had over the course of writing this book it's been a fascinating experience. And, Paul, you may have tried to sue me, you may have tried to punch me, you may have even, on one occasion, put a photo of Joseph Goebbels through my letterbox, but I don't hold any grudges. You are what you are. That's your job. Being you. Someone's got to do it. And you do it so well.

Shadows of Reflections

Foreword by Paul Hamilton

With regard to the poems included in *Shadows of Reflections* I spent some six weeks deliberating over what criterion should dictate the order of their presentation. Degree of pain involved in their conception? Philosophical bent at the time of writing? Theme (i.e. Loss, Redemption, Seafood, etc.)? In the end, unusually for me, I opted for the conventional. I decided to present them in chronological order.

What you are about to read, as far as I am concerned, is the only part of the book/Kindle file you are holding that truly matters.

These poems tell the true story of my life. The rest – the anecdotes, the recollections – is but dust in the wind.

I hope you like them.

I wrote them for you.

Acceptance

This was the first 'real' poem I ever wrote. Up until then I had been posing. I wrote it in less than a week. When I'd finished it I felt so pleased with it that I was actually worried. I decided to put it away for a week and then look at it again with fresh eyes. When I looked at it again I wanted to sit down. But I was already sitting down, so I had to lie down! I knew that for once I had written something that didn't make me want to go down to the canal and drink gin under a bridge.

Although it is entitled 'Acceptance' it's actually about rejection. The rejection of all those mindsets that don't recognise acceptance. I suppose I could just as easily have called it 'Rejection', but then that would actually be leading the reader or listener away from the fact that it's the concept of acceptance which forms the bedrock on which the theme of rejection is implicitly explored.

And I do have muffins. If you ever happen to drop by.

I always have muffins.

ACCEPTANCE

Hirsute lesbian: I love you.
Freedom's guerrilla: I salute you.
Bipolar Inuit: I embrace you.
Come you all to my home.
I have muffins.

God's Terrorists

Generally, it is never my intention to rock the boat for rocking the boat's sake. So believe me when I tell you that I never set out to cause controversy with this one. Actually, if I'd known the kind of trouble it was going to get me into maybe I'd have censored myself a little.

Wait a minute.

Who am I kidding?

Religious fundamentalism is obviously a pretty hot potato. A lot of poets won't touch it with a barge pole. And who can blame them? It's entirely possible that in some holy book or other physical contact between a heated root vegetable and a long wooden stick is highly blasphemous and punishable by some kind of hideous death or another. I wouldn't be surprised.

I couldn't hold back on this one, though.

The inspiration for this poem came about when I was taking part in a quiz night at my local. During the break between the first and second rounds these guys came into the pub and started making their way around the tables. I was suspicious because they looked so incongruous in a pub setting. Everything about them seemed alien. Their demeanour, their clothes, the way they spoke. When one of them reached our table I realised exactly what they were. Members of the Salvation Army. I was asked if I wanted to buy a copy of their newspaper, the *War Cry*. I enquired what the money would be used for. The reply came back: 'We use the money people kindly give us to run charity shops, shelters for the homeless and to provide disaster relief and humanitarian aid for developing countries.' And it was blindingly obvious that what he wanted to go on to say was 'rather than sitting around, drinking alcohol and trying to answer questions about pop-chart entries in 1975'. But that is entirely by the by. At the time, as far as I was concerned, it seemed pretty obvious that the slightly quaint Victorian exterior of the Salvation Army was just a cover-up for a pretty heavy mind-control agenda. Let's put this in context, though. I was a very angry man at the time. I was very down on religion. My whole experience of it since childhood had been very negative, from *Songs of Praise* to 'Sir' Cliff Richard. The local vicar used to occasionally visit my mother when I was a child, and his flatulence was so bad she'd have the windows open for the rest of the day. I caught pleurisy once as a result of him coming round in the middle of a cold snap. So I bought a copy of this Salvation Army man's *War Cry*, used my biro to scrub out 'War' and wrote 'Peace' instead, and handed it back to him. I got quite a look, I can tell you.

I've done some research on the Salvation Army since, and if they do have a programme in place to make the entire world Salvationist, then it's pretty well hidden. But it would be, wouldn't it?

I've certainly moderated my view on religion over the years. I'm not quite so on its case. Some people just need to keep on sucking that dummy, that's all. However, the simple fact remains that there are people out there who hold to a world view which they believe to be the entire truth, and any deviation from that truth in some way makes you 'the enemy', to be despised, or even eradicated. Well, listen up. How about this? I'll stick to my beliefs and you stick to yours. Even if they do stink to high heaven.

Which, incidentally, doesn't actually exist.

Out on the streets they are trying to charm me.
They're playing their music but it doesn't calm me.
They're evil, they're killers, they're liars, they're smarmy,
They're coming to your town – the Salvation Army.

Yeah, the tambourine's cool and the sousaphone's pretty,
They send out a message of love and of pity
But if you think they're good, then you're like Walter
    Mitty.
Oh! The Salvation Army!

Uniforms, marching, moustaches are clues.
Doesn't it sound like familiar news?
Where is it that you will never find Jews?
Yes, the Salvation Army.

Since they first started out oh the lives they have shattered,
World domination is all that has mattered.
They're offering you God but please don't be flattered,
Their message is cod and they should be battered –
the Salvation Army.

Closure

Glynis Donald was a terrific poet who used to regularly come and do readings of her poetry at 'Word Up'. She was a true eccentric, already in her mid-sixties when I first met her in 1993. She had had quite a life. First published in the early fifties, she had pre-dated Plath by some ten years with some very bleak stuff about women's problems. Her initial downfall was the bottle. Unhappily married to a philandering racehorse owner, she was a hopeless alcoholic by the end of the fifties. After being divorced by her husband she lost custody of her two children, Belinda and Graham.

By the end of the sixties she had kicked the booze entirely but was now a heroin addict. By the end of the seventies she'd come off the smack and was back on the sauce. By the end of the eighties she had successfully beaten her reliance on liquor and scag and had become a registered sex addict. By the time I met her she was back on the hootch and occasionally mainlining junk yet again. In spite of all this she was always very upbeat, very positive.

I had only known her a year when disaster struck. She had not long been reunited with her estranged daughter Belinda. They had met a few times and got on tolerably well. Belinda had her own demons to deal with and was being treated for morbid obesity due to her addiction to trifle. One awful summer's evening Belinda had been sitting at the wheel of the narrowboat her mother lived on. Whenever she visited her mother she would always beg to be allowed to take the boat for a little spin, and thoroughly enjoyed steering the boat as it puttered gently along Regent's Canal. Glynis had just popped below deck to fetch a fresh bottle of brandy when Belinda carelessly caused the narrowboat to clip the bow of a boat coming the other way. As a result of the ensuing jolt she lost her balance and fell overboard, sinking immediately, even though she was wearing a lifejacket. Truly tragic.

One evening, not long after, I had taken Glynis to my favourite Italian restaurant in Highgate. (And it is still my favourite. It's called Vittorio's. Ask for Teodoro. Tell him Mr Hamilton sent you and do not fail to order the bucatini amatriciana.) Anyway, I'd taken her there to commiserate, my treat, and afterwards, outside the restaurant, as she was holding my hand and wailing, I remember looking down as I nodded my acknowledgement of her agony and seeing a piece of spinach on her finger. It's odd. I can see it even today. It is no more than an eighth of an inch square. In almost filmic slow motion it is transferred from her finger to my thumb. It must have come from her cannelloni dish. In that moment I saw that piece of spinach as her grief. Her pain. Her despair. The poem kind of wrote itself after that.

CLOSURE

And when you touched me in Highgate,
you left a piece of spinach on my thumb knuckle,
green and dead, like your daughter Belinda.
Oh, Glynis, it was not your fault she fell from the barge
and yet you will ever grieve and curse your failure to
    save her.
And when I had left you I walked home and,
passing an old church wall, with tears of joy
and a sense of unimpeachable victory
I scraped the spinach against the moss.
Weep no more, Glynis . . .
The moss has taken her.

Prejudice

I, Paul Hamilton, am a pretentious, self-obsessed, airy-fairy bore.

Well, I must be. After all, I am a poet.

How often do we do this? Make a snap judgement about something or someone based on nothing more than a collection of clichés that have been crammed into our heads by the press or advertisements or the media in general?

I know a black guy who dances like Michael Howard. I know a lesbian who doesn't like sex with women. I know a dwarf who's not a drunk. I know a Catholic priest who is not a paedophile. I know a Frenchman who does not smell. I know an American who is not a brain-dead moron. I could go on.

It is vital that we not let ourselves think in terms of clichés. We need to not rush to judgement but instead start thinking outside the box and reading between the lines, because, let's face it, haste makes waste.

PREJUDICE

My friend Alistair McCardie has ginger hair.
He eats porridge for breakfast.
He is, to be truthful, cautious with his money.
He drinks whisky, enjoys football and the skirl of the
    pipes.
My friend Alistair McCardie

is Welsh.

Dream

This was the direct result of a dream I had one night which was remarkably vivid. In it Sophie and I were a king and queen at some unspecified time in the past, although I'd put it somewhere in the middle of the medieval era.

I'm keeping an open mind about the origins of this poem. It could be that my subconscious was presenting Sophie and me in terms of archetypes. The king represents masculine maturity. He is powerful in his own realm and is not only creative but inspires creativity in others. The queen represents strong feminine traits: the ability to discern and champion the absolute truth whilst at the same time possessing the flexibility to adopt an entirely opposite point of view in the blink of an eye.

Then again, could it be that I was somehow remembering some past life? The vividness of the dream stayed with me for a long time. Here's a truly inexplicable thing: in the dream I remember smelling my fingers and, as the king, recognising the odour of wild boar fat. Before the dream I had never encountered wild boar in any way, and that includes smelling its fat. You can imagine my astonishment when some months later I did smell wild boar fat (at the Trowbridge real-ale festival in Wiltshire) and found that it smelled exactly, but *exactly* the same as it had in my dream.

Life's mysteries. They are manifold. We may not be able to explain them, even though we are urged to try. I say leave them be. They add a little magic to our existence.

Sophie thinks this poem is rich in phallic imagery – the marrow, the lute, the pointed beard – but quite frankly she could see a penis in a barrel of vaginas.

Whatever the explanation, it is one of Sophie's favourites and, like you could say *Wings of Desire* is 'our' film and 'You Are So Beautiful' is 'our' song, I suppose you could say 'Dream' is 'our' poem.

DREAM

Last night I did dream, fair Sophie,
that I, a king with pointed beard and golden crown,
beroofed with empurpled burlap,
did gaze at thee with love whilst thou, my queen,
perched upon golden cushions, did feast upon a pick-
    led marrow.
And, my dove, as all our happy realm knelt upon its
    gladsome knee,
to the thrumming of the lute I did sing:
Fa-la-la, my pretty maiden.
Fa-la-la, my pretty one!

Wave Crime

Whoever it was that said poetry has to be all navel-gazing seriousness is a prize buffoon. I quite often find that taking a wry look at situations in a poem can not only raise a chuckle here and there, but can do so without lessening its impact or reducing its power to make the reader think a little bit about the subject matter. This poem came about after one of those lucky moments we poets can sometimes have, when we're experiencing something quite normal and our perception of it shifts in an unexpected direction, providing a whole new take on the familiar.

We were at dinner round the house of someone who is actually quite famous. (I'm not going to name-drop. I've never been one to be impressed by fame, as I think I've already stated. I once accidentally nearly knocked over Gloria Hunniford in a branch of John Lewis. I apologised to her no more and no less than I would have to anyone else.) Anyway, this celebrity always puts on a nice spread, and as his wife served a fish dish she happened to comment that her husband found her sauce 'seductive'. It prompted me to ponder on the sheer sensuousness that is involved in good eating and how there is something a little bit 'naughty' in the enjoyment of it. I actually had to excuse myself from the table before the meal had begun and find a quiet spot and start work on the poem, until I had at least squeezed out a rough first draft. If a poem is coming it just takes over everything. I have to grasp the idea before it melts back into the ether. Whatever else I'm doing at the time becomes completely irrelevant. I have worried before now about what would happen if I were ever struck by the muse halfway through giving mouth-to-mouth resuscitation. What would I do? Surely the answer is obvious?

I'm not so sure.

WAVE CRIME

Ocean.

Great ocean!

Briny behemoth, tide-torn titan, hear my confession!

Tonight I feasted upon one of your piscine progeny.

Without shame, but without malice.

Oh, mother of the fishes! Oh, that you could understand and forgive . . .

Seduction by almond and tarragon sauce.

Spain

I'm very proud of this one. Sophie and I were going through a little bit of a rough patch. There was blame on both sides, and yet no one was out to start trouble; it's just the way things were hanging. I'd been flirting for a number of weeks with shamanism, and quite frankly I was feeling a little detached from normality. Meanwhile, Sophie had just undergone a particularly nasty procedure to remove an ingrowing toenail. So when she suggested we fly to Madrid for the weekend, I was simply in no frame of mind to even consider it: booking the flights, digging out trunks, buying suntan lotion, plus, of course, Sophie was on a crutch – it just wasn't what I wanted or could even begin to deal with at the time.

This poem is actually, word for word, something I said to her in Waitrose on the Holloway Road. We'd been arguing about the trip. We were by the condiments shelf. As I stated my case I knew that I was uttering more than just some passing comments as soon as I'd said them. Unusually, I didn't have any paper or pencil with me and so, fearful that I would forget exactly what I had said, I quickly wrote it on the nearest jar of pickled gherkins with a marker pen I borrowed from a passing shop assistant. I still have the jar. Sophie ate the gherkins.

'Spain' is about self-determination. It's about conviction. I never did go to Spain, and do you know what? I don't think I ever will.

SPAIN

I've no wish to go to Spain.
No wish at all.
And I shan't go.
I shan't.

Tribute to Justin Wiverly

Justin Wiverly was a debauched, drug-taking lecher who thought only about himself. In every situation that he ever found himself he only and always behaved entirely reprehensibly.

What a guy.

I think every craftsman, artist or philosopher must have a mentor. Someone who inspires. Someone who coaxes the very best out of his acolyte. I found just that in this extraordinary, never-to-be-repeated phenomenon. I would look at Justin lying comatose in an airing cupboard, face smeared with blood, trousers wet with urine, and think, 'That is what I aspire to.'

I would listen to Justin, half on and half off the top of a bus shelter, shouting at the top of his voice to anyone within hearing range in a made-up language, and I would think, 'There is my ideal.'

I would flinch from Justin as he threw fruit, crockery and anything else that came to hand whilst traducing me in the foulest terms imaginable because I was wearing the shirt I was wearing, and I would think, 'This is what I must be.'

I speak, of course, of the purity of his spirit. Of the uncompromising nature of his convictions. Of his total, unceasing immersion in all the stuff of life.

You weasels of mediocrity!

You minnows of conformity!

You sloths of banality!

From beyond the grave Justin Wiverly wishes a pox on you and yours.

Seconded.

Justin, you wrote with bent and swollen fingers
of epilepsy in the park and your biting mother.
And who could forget your 'Impressions of Surgery'
written under local anaesthetic during The Gallstone
    Years.
And when at last your great heart
could no longer swing to the beat
you died unpublished.
Unpublished.
Unpublished.
Unpublished.
Unpublished.
Unpublished.
Unpublished.
Unpublished.
And although you died a gasping, thrashing death –
'No more, dear God, no more . . .' –
I rejoice that you died with poetry in your ears
and I am proud that it was mine.

Goose Step

As I always point out in my preamble at live readings, this poem has a Yuletide theme, but the message is pan-seasonal.

I got talking one evening to a guy at Taekwondo who had worked at a small independent goose farm. Initially he had enjoyed his job immensely. He fed and watered the geese and made sure there was fresh hay in their coops and that their roaming space was clean and well tended. But when it came to Christmas, the whole nature of his job changed. Then, it was one of his duties to throttle the geese and put them in a vat ready for plucking. When the first Christmas came along, he had only been there for a few months and had not formed too close a bond with the birds. The second was very, very much harder and he had only just about got through the whole ordeal by anaesthetising himself with large amounts of vodka. By the third Christmas he had become so emotionally involved with the birds, giving them names and even discerning individual personalities in them, that he had some sort of breakdown, took a shotgun and held the goose farmer and his wife hostage in their house for three days before being shot in the thigh by a police marksman. He was sent to jail for seven years.

He was, all in all, a broken man, still haunted by the atrocities he had been obliged to perform on his feathered charges. Apparently, just before a goose dies, it emits a 'death honk', and it was this noise that filled every hour of his sleep at night.

May that noise never scar your eardrums.

Christmas is coming the geese are getting fat
And then they're being strangled and thrown into a
   vat.
Enjoy your meal.

Time

What time is it? Or, more to the point, what is it, time? Is it a man-made construct, like cabin windows or wing nuts? Or is it a naturally occurring phenomenon, like oxbow lakes or yoghurt?

Does time have a smell? A colour? A texture?

It is some nine seconds since you started reading this page. Assuming you had at least a halfway decent education. Or are not suffering from dyslexia, in which case forgive me.

Consider this:

You will never get those seconds back.

Tick tock. Tick tock.

Time is a fascinating and complex subject that has fascinated not only me but also Einstein and the scientific and philosophical greats for absolutely yonks. And yet still, after all this, well, time, I personally am no closer to fully understanding it.

I don't think I am alone in that regard.

At the time of writing this poem I was in my early thirties and quite frankly terrified of death. The thought of a slow, painful process of disintegration preceding a final, inescapable descent into an eternal darkness filled me with a dread that formed a deeply angst-ridden backdrop to my whole life. I think, looking back, this explains some of the intestinal disorders.

No more, though. For the last ten years or so I have been taking a minute each and every day to openly laugh at death. At noon, wherever I am, whatever I am doing, I laugh out loud at the Grim Reaper for exactly sixty seconds.

I hope I die laughing.

TIME

Time, like a rancid stallion,
gallops along the bridle path of our rotting lives.
Whinnying or loseying, we are all saddled,
spurred on by time's hoof, I am the dying proof.
Time, ay, you time, you, you, time, you tie me,
time, to me, aye, time, you, time, you tie tiny me,
time, you, time, you tie me, tiny, tiny me, time, to me.
Time.

Writer's Block

This was, ironically, the poem that brought an end to a bout of writer's block that held me in its steely grip for over four years.

Imagine you're a pole-vaulter and someone takes your pole away.

Think about being a dancer and having your feet cut off and then force-fed to you.

Consider being a DJ and having no button to press.

Pretty grim scenarios.

But not a hundredth as calamitous as my experience of not being able to come up with a single solitary line of poetry for four whole years.

There's always something potentially poetical percolating in my brain, in my heart, in my guts. It may be just a vague glimmer of an idea. It may be a visual image. It may be a phrase. It may just be a word. It can even be a letter. The letter W popping into my mind led me to write the poem 'W' in 2000 after a certain election across the pond:

Weak, wicked, witless, woolly, weedy, woeful, wormy,
watery, wasteful, wooden, work-shy wino.
Wearisome, whittering, wacko wally.
White-washing, word-warping, war-waging wanker.
W.
George W.

Remember that guy?

Anyway, I digress. For four years I had nothing. Every thought in my mind was functional and pragmatic: 'Buy more lettuce'; 'Clean behind the aquarium'; 'Read the article on Proust.' There were plenty of those kinds of thoughts. Too many. But nary a single consideration that came even close to subverting perception, illuminating conundra or questioning givens. It wasn't until I became a poet that I realised that I have always had at least some kind of imaginative exploration going on somewhere in my interior life. As a small child I remember that even as I read the early reading Janet and John books I would imagine that their voices were screeching and cacophonous in timbre. Closer to squawks than human voices. Of course, when I read what they said out loud in class in that voice, the teacher told me to 'stop being ridiculous'. And this is what state education did, and still does, to any kid showing a little bit of alternative creativity. Closes them down.

I have no idea how the non-poet can live with a mental process that is basically a to-do list. I can only assume that if that's the way you have always thought, then it must be in some way bearable. No wonder that to a certain extent I became insane during this time. It was a quiet, restrained sort of insanity, but insanity nonetheless.

As I have explained, it was Sophie who saved me. I was lost, and she found me. When she took me to her bed the night she dragged me out of that awful wedding reception I was playing at, she turned me on in more than one way. I still remember the morning after. Realising that something had returned. Reaching for the pad. Taking up the pen and in one slow but sure flourish writing my first poem in four years, two hundred and three days and seventeen hours. When Sophie came out of the toilet, I wordlessly handed it to her. We'd wept quite a bit throughout that night, but that was when the weeping started in earnest.

Reader, I'm weeping right now.

WRITER'S BLOCK

I have writer's block.

The Not So Great Dictator

In 2005 Sophie and I visited China for a holiday. It was pretty amazing. We saw some terrific sights. Apart from one occasion when we were offered hummingbird to eat, we had a wonderful time. 'What a country,' we thought. 'What a set-up.' Communism in action and, boy, did it look good.

We were reeled in, hook, line and rickshaw.

Just a month after I got back I watched a documentary about Mao on the History Channel. It was then that I realised that we had in fact visited an illusory Shangri-La created by the brutal whims of a certifiable maniac.

I lost a very dear communist friend as a result of this poem. I gave it to him to read. He spat on it, ripped it into tiny pieces and then threw the pieces in my face. I asked him what he meant by his actions. He replied that he did not like the poem. We argued long and hard. It became very bitter. I accused him of wilful intransigence. He accused me of betraying a great cause. I accused him of head-in-the-clouds idealism. He accused me of being 'a shit poet'. It was when his argument descended to this level of brainless slander that our friendship ended for ever. It is a great shame.

I stand by the poem, even though I'm not sure I'd ever dare to travel to China again now that it has finally been published.

I blame the fat guy with the mole.

Mao! Mao! Where are you now, Mao?
Zedong?
Cat got your tongue?
Chairman, you weren't a fair man.
You turned communism into conyouism
And now your *Little Red Book* is a little-read book.
As the people did cower the poisonous shower
from the cloud of your power killed liberty's flower.
You bloody bastard.

Tony Blair's Contribution to World Peace

I voted for that cheesy freak in '97. Hell, didn't we all? And then he went and turned the Labour Party into the Tory Party and rode straight into an illegal war alongside the brain-dead cowboy I alluded to three pages back.

Way to go, Tony.

TONY BLAIR'S CONTRIBUTION TO WORLD PEACE

Hate Date

This piece was the direct result of a particularly rancorous tiff between Sophie and me. I can't remember what it was about. Probably something to do with Afghanistan, but at any rate she ended up moving out for a few weeks. I was in a pretty angry frame of mind and decided that I'd get my own back on her by seeing another woman. Childish. Anyway, it's the first and last time I've ever resorted to online dating. I got chatting to this interesting-sounding woman, and we really seemed to get on. I found her frankness and down-to-earth approach to life very refreshing. Sadly, she was perhaps a little over-fond of refreshments generally and, face to face at a soirée for two in my Islington flat, what had seemed to be charming directness in a virtual room turned out to be boorish philistinism in a real one.

Needless to say, there wasn't a repeat rendezvous!

HATE DATE

You didn't like my gooseberry wine,
You said you'd rather lager.
You said what's wrong with microwaves
And sneered at my old aga.
You would not watch *Wings of Desire*,
The movie by Wim Wenders.
Instead the shrieking cockney angst,
The foulness of *EastEnders*.
My shirt, my hair, my Rothko prints
All claimed your disapproval.
Even my best underpants
After trouser removal.
It surely was not love we made
And not from heaven sent.
You vomited my mango flan,
You came and came, came one more time,
You punched my cat, then went.

Roadside Genocide

I travel up and down the country by car a lot, going to my various poetry readings. I don't drive myself. Sophie takes the wheel, bless her, and I usually put on one of the CDs I have in a series called *Nature's Voices*. The sound of flamingos in flight, a Hebridean wind, pandas' mating cries – there are many different sounds to suit many different moods. This allows me to relax and prepare for the upcoming performance.

The one thing that truly depresses me, though, is the carnage I see on our roads. It seems that on some roads every few hundred yards or so are the grisly remains of some poor creature that's been flattened by some speeding idiot. Sure, accidents do happen. A finch may be startled out of the hedgerow by a crack of thunder and fly straight into the path of an oncoming lorry. A cat, delirious with bloodlust at the sight of a chick that's fallen out of a nest on the other side of the road, may tragically end its life under the wheels of a milk float. But . . . but . . . may we not drive just a little less frenetically? A little more carefully?

I've deliberately accentuated the horrific details of this sickening phenomenon because people need to know the full graphic consequences of their actions. In the final stanza it was my intention to give these animals a voice where they have none.

Let's stop this.

ROADSIDE GENOCIDE

Hey!
What's black and white and red all over?
A magpie hit by a brand-new Rover.
And that's not funny, it's a bird all runny.

And what about the others all now gone?
The list goes on and on and on.

A rook with both its eyes squashed out,
An owl with entrails strewn about.
And on and on and on and on.
What once was a mouse is now a stain,
And ooh, just look, it's a puppy dog's brain.
And on and on and on. What's that?
A rabbit in the habit of being alive,
Till it got hit by a Mazda 5.
And on and on and on and on.

But wait!

What's this in the road up ahead?
An accident and the driver's dead.
And by the road stands an orphaned vole,
And he laughs and shouts from the depth of his soul:
'Aha haha haha har!
Death to the driver, death to the car!'
Roadside, roadside genocide.
Roadside genocide.
Drive carefully.

On Remonstrating with the Alcoholic about His Comments on the Barmaid from Poland

This is just a very sad little poem, I think. Based, like nearly all of my pieces, entirely on a real experience.

There is a terrific little pub near our flat that I like to pop into occasionally for a pie and a pint. It has none of that Sky Sports unpleasantness and has a terrific range of crisp flavours. Adrian (not his real name) was a local who had come into some money in his early forties and since then had spent most days ensconced at the bar, reading his red top and engaging anyone who would listen in idle banter. He was perhaps not the most sophisticated of fellows and, one day, much the worse for wear, he tried to inveigle me into some sort of leering Neanderthal exchange concerning the barmaid who had recently started working there. There is no doubt that she was very attractive, but I thought his remarks disrespectful and told him so in no uncertain terms.

This poem is the result of the dressing down I gave him on this occasion.

Very much to my surprise, he and the barmaid went on to marry. They now have twins and are living in Lublin.

ON REMONSTRATING WITH THE ALCOHOLIC
ABOUT HIS COMMENTS ON THE BARMAID
FROM POLAND

No, Adrian.
I will not 'get a load of that Polish bit'.
No, Adrian, I would not like to
'get my head between those two beauties and go wuba
    wuba wuba'.
No, Adrian.
Adrian, no.
Adrian, there are Greggs pastry flakes in your beard
and vomit on your shoes and dandruff in your hair.
Adrian, there are Pringles in your larder and urine in
    your milk bottles
and a Vauxhall Astra engine in your bed.
Adrian, there is nothing in your diary and something
    in your attic,
and I don't know what that is in your toilet.
Adrian, when you look at Anna Zowlski (she has a
    name),
you see 3D, page-three, swinging free, double-D fantasy
through the lies of your lager-filled eyes.
Whereas I, I see a brave young woman in a cowardly
    old town
who yearns for her mama's goulash.

Perhaps That's Where You're Going Wrong

I often 'do the festivals', as they say. There are some lovely little affairs all around the country these days. There's the Peasant's Festival near Devizes, the Mead Festival in Polperro, the Wheat Dolly Festival in Pebmarsh – all of which offer some wonderfully diverse ethnic music, arts and crafts stalls and quite often a poetry tent. They are charming and there's always something for all ages.

This poem was literally born in the heat of the night. It came about during a disastrous stay at one of the larger festivals, the Tripathon Festival near Guildford. Sophie and I had the misfortune to pitch our tent next to a group of thoroughly obnoxious people. I mean, come on, sure, it's a festival, let your hair down, go crazy. I'm no stuffed shirt. But these jokers were still partying hard and way, way too loud at half past one in the bloody morning.

There was one particular yob whose voice cut above all the others, and it was his repeated avowal of his detestation of a particular foodstuff that kick-started me into writing what is most definitely one of my angriest poems.

De-civilised by a cocktail of chemicals,
They are low not high.
'I hate fucking coriander,' shrieks one.
'I hate fucking coriander,' he re-shrieks.
'I hate fucking coriander,' he shrieks on for thirty-
    seven minutes.
'Well, don't fuck it then,' I finally mutter and then write
    that down,
Here on this piece of paper, now, in this tent, taking
    consolation that
Out of even extreme adversity, some good may come.
Oh, shrieking troll in your canvas lair of invidious
    hominids, do not hate that pungent herb,
Do not hate that aromatic denizen of the East.
Hate war,
Hate injustice,
Hate hate.
But do not hate coriander.
Perhaps that's where you're going wrong.

I Am a Dalek

Justin Wiverly was resolutely adamant that this poem was by far the finest piece of work I ever produced. I'm not entirely convinced I personally agree with him on that but then again who am I to argue with the master? And so on Justin's recommendation, and that's good enough for me, I leave you with this final poem.

I'm not sure I can explain it. I'm not sure I should. It just slipped out of me one night like a newborn foal. Whatever you take from it, you're welcome to it and you don't need to bring it back.

I AM A DALEK

I am a dalek.
No, literally.